For the second time, we have gathered together a representative collection of the best of the poetry that has been published in the regional high school and college anthologies, during the past five years.

These that were considered worthy of publication in a bound volume, have been culled from over ond hundred annual anthologies. Many of the young authors have now left school to establish a place in the world for themselves. Without the encouragement of their teachers and the atmosphere of the scholastic surroundings, the urge to create may be subordinated to the needs and demands of existence in these fast-moving times.

It is our hope that, in presenting the work of these authors, we are giving to them a breath of the "white hyacinths" that will satisfy their poetic souls. If we accomplish this purpose, we are content.

Dennis Hartman, Editor

Westside Village
Los Angeles 34
California
June, 1955

VOICE OF YOUNG AMERICA

To Barbara
from a piece of page 124
Virginia

1951-1955

NATIONAL POETRY ASSOCIATION
Los Angeles 34, California

VOICE OF AMERICA

SONNET TO YOUTH   Earle Griffin

Please, do not think when you are gone away
And your desires no longer burn in me,
That I upon some bright, oblivious day
Shall slander you with fickle memory.
Though I should ache with want a thousand ways,
This craving for possession in my heart
Will pierce my mind 'til weary, feeble days
Whisper at last my summons to depart.

Let earth defile these hungry years with jest
Leaving their meager wraps to swift decay;
I'll clasp each shrivelled morsel to my breast,
Lest, fed from richer harvests on a day
When loaves of plenty heap upon my plate
I quite forget the stubble that we ate.

DO NOT LAUGH   Carol Patterson

I admit that I am young,
Inexperienced,
Naive, neglectful of others,
Insignificant.

But who are you, pompous silly man,
Self-satisfied, self-indulgent,
To laugh at me?
To say that I am giddy and foolish
In my adolescence?

Have you done better?
Have you, in middle age,
Fulfilled that wild, surging hope
Which God in your promising childhood
Entrusted to you?

Yes, I am young.
But I shall build my life upward,
Not downward.
Nor shall I mock at those who try their wings.

Only futility mocks at aspiration.

DESERT PLAINS   Charles Morgan

... And o'er the wind-swept desert plains,
Silence, with his weird companions, Stillness and Solitude, dominates ...
Only to be clashing again and again with his opposite,
The Wind, who constantly argues that sands need alternate smoothings,
And who receives in answered stillness a powerful force of serenity ....

And seemingly a barrier caused by Sol,
Who looks down, radiating a concentrated heat.
In an amusement upon the Wind and sands, ... and Silence,
Making a mortal life unbearable and impossible.

But still the peace, though in heat and warm brown sands,
Makes one hold and think what joy in such quietness;
This is a haven in itself, from all the noises,
All around over the wind-swept desert Plains.

FANTASY   Pat Faust

What a small world we do live in!
With people all about us.
Swarming, storming, in a spin,
Running about and making a fuss.

We always thought that we were tops,
While others would stand still.
But now we find we're only flops,
While the others destiny fulfill.

The bell of the ball in one's small world,
The queen of fantasy and dreams,
To awake to reality as though hurled,
Away in thought to me it seems.

REGRET   Bunny Duskin

How strange, my dear, that when we meet,
My once fond heart has ceased to beat
So madly at our fingerstouch.
Your voice that used to mean so much,
And seemed a liquid, silver stream,
No longer sets my mind to dream
Of an enchanted life with you.
For the magic fairy-tale is through.
The bubbling seas of love, somewhere,
Have turned to vapor, a mist in air.
And though I feel a vague regret,
My dear, I do not really fret,
For soon my memories I'll erase ...
With another one to take your place.

A PRELUDE   John Gyer

The air is clear, and crisp, and cold.
The clouds have halted in their flight.
The sun is sinking slowly in the west
Shedding all the glory of its light,
Touching yonder hills, their highest peaks, with gold.
The day is dying. It is old.
And so, when we ourselves grow old
And settle down to rest,
Fear not for we, as day, shall surely wake again
And rise and live with harmony and peace with all.
We are not all angels yet, but we can gain.
Look not on death as a blank wall.
For life is just a transient form,
But death is a great prelude to the dawn.

BEYOND   Marie Therese Klocker

When earth extends her arms to take the dead,
It's not for me the closing of a grave;
But rather, resting upon Nature's bed
And reflecting whether I my soul did save.
When friends cry useless tears and for me mourn,
I think, "Oh, why not save your tears and pray!"
And even though your hearts are cruelly torn,
Weep not for me but for yourselves this day.
For I have gone to my own destiny,
While you on earth still fear His righteous wrath;
I share in happy bliss for all Eternity,
While you, my loved, must trod the narrow path.
And in His tender mercy and His love,
You will someday find our Home Above.

HERALD OF SPRING   Dottie Harroun

At last winter is gone
And spring reigns supreme.
Each daffodil opes and the lark
Sings on high to the dawn,
And beneath on the lawn
The robin doth hark
To the song.

He flits in the sunshine,
And flies to the branch
Of a low hanging flowering tree.
He seems a sure sign,
This robin of mine,
And my heart cries with glee
For 'tis spring!

12

DESERT SCENE   Marietta O'Farrell

Arid waters of great expanse
The lure of shiny gold -
Shifting sands do all entrance
Man's heart to dare the bold.

Like a ruthless fire the day goes by
But night steals cooling down
While starlight-lantern illumined sky
Casts moonbeams toward the ground.

A prospector all bend and gray
Breaks the line where land meets sky
A coyote's howl heralds dying day
To hollow out the wasteland's cry.

CLOUDS   Mary Jane Griffiths

The roaring clouds pile swiftly, darkly high.
They roll in surging waves from mountain crags,
Unfurling sails that sweep across the sky -
As black-blown banners, conqueror's dusty flags.
The clouds, in columns, climb the soundless air,
As driven now by screaming winds, they grow
And swirl - a goddess trailing tangled hair.
They come with haste, a heavy, laden flow.

But suddenly, a power halts the whirling skies,
And silence falls, and reigns as tumult fades.
The sunshine softly opens dazzling eyes
And glows bright golden under darker shades.
The earth lies breathless 'neath this train.
And then, the heavens stir. Here comes the rain.

WHERE HAPPINESS IS FOUND   Ruta Lukas-
                          Lukas'evic'iute'
"What are you looking for?" I ask.
You promptly answer, "Love."
"Then do not look upon the earth,
Because it is above."

"It's justice that we want to find,
And peace," so many cry.
"It is not here," I say again,
"You have to look on high.

"For never will you reach your goal,
And find these things, unless
To Heavenly Father you appeal
For love and happiness."

FOR FRANCES, WRITTEN AT DUSK   Bill Tuning

Across the dimm'd blue arch of sky
The twilight paths of light lead on, whereby
They come to the sunset's garland on the hills
Shedding soft cloudy light on one lone bird
Who fills the dusk with reedy, flutelike trills;
But his little song is naught till it is heard
By someone there in the soft, translucent light . . .
That loveliest of times - after the day and before the night.

The silent dusk when there is no sound
Was made for the love that my love may say with a look,
When we have at twilight the harsh day forsook;
And my love that may so silently resound,
Where the cloudy-colored sunset flowers abound,
Is my love of you, and the twilight that knows no sound.

SONNET OF A TIGER CAT   Mary Ada Woodward

A vivid yellow streak cuts through the black
But melts into a silvered frothy sheen
As it is met by icy spheres of green
Intent upon the object of attack.
A whisp of purest white trails toward her back,
Though soon 'tis lost in clouds of tangerine.
Ferocity forgotten, she will preen,
Then sleep in some small, unobtrusive crack.
A faltering "meeow" lilts through the air;
One inky paw enticingly extends;
She purrs. Ah, now you're lured into her snare!
Her loving eyes belie that she pretends,
But when she tires of your being there
She'll flash an ivory claw: deception ends.

JEWELS   Nancy Magnusson

Jewels scattered upon a page,
Each drawing a different pattern.
Some tell of sorrow and others of glory,
But all form an exquisite story.

Diamonds that sing a gay, sparkling tune,
And pearls that are smooth and clear.
Sapphires of night and of quiet sleep,
And emeralds that hum of the deep.

A melody sung with infinite thought,
Expressed by these jeweled notes,
Molded together - a symphony,
That blends into perfect harmony.

SPRING   Kenneth Weeks

Awaken now you little birds of blue
Send out a sweet refrain ringing clear.
In the lonely garden all wet with dew,
Again it is the spring time of the year.
Down by the garden wall all bathed in rain
You gather bits of straw for little nests;
Then up to the lofty boughs you fly again;
Children of nature, never a minute of rest.
Awake, you little flowers, do not die,
Show signs of life; lift fragrant little heads.
The song of spring is nature's only cry.
To give forth color to the flower beds,
Nature has pushed aside the heavy door.
Sweet Spring is here to greet us all once more.

SCRUBBING A DIRTY FLOOR   Carole Behmler

There's seen a blackness to my scanning eye,
    A gloomy blackness that invites a cure,
A duty that to me oft proves a lure.
    And from the depths I seem to hear a cry
To free it from this curse; I will hard try
    To make the floor again look shining pure,
To see its brightest light again I'm sure.
    Then to the cupboard for the pail I fly
To start again the chore I never fear,
    A chore which to me proves again success,
For 'neath my hand the black will disappear,
    And this does give to me, no less,
A feeling of success I hold so dear;
    I thank the floor for this I now possess.

Eleanor Powers

The world began when I was born.
The sun shone first and light was new;
I saw the sky in its first blue,
And I saw first the dawn of morn;
I walked in Eden that was shorn
Of all its drab and tarnished hue;
For me alone was earth made new,
And came to be when I was born.
The summer wind blew first for me;
I heard first a robin's song
As hills were formed before my eyes;
I first knew the painful ecstasy
Of life, its lilting song, its sighs.
The world will end when I am gone.

SONNET I   Joseph F. Meara

If men the glory of the bards do praise,
Revere the yellowed pages from their hand,
Which though preserved in artificial ways,
The crumbling hand of time can not withstand,
If men enshrine with legend in their hearts,
The fabled deeds of heroes passed to dust,
And homage outwardly to them impart
With monuments assailed by rack and rust,
Then should they not as babe to mother clings,
The words of truth eternal cherish dear,
And honor Him who, unlike earthly kings,
Presides through love and not by dint of fear?
And how much more should permeate the soul
The love for Him whose vision is our goal.

STORM   Mary Lou Blanchard

Thunder is the voice of an angry God
Rumbling a warning to the puny things of earth.
He calls his army of clouds;
Dressed in their somber uniforms of grey,
Hiding the face of the peaceful sun,
They march forward,
Blinding the enemy with their lightning shells.

Going suddenly as they had come,
With another shout of victory, they disappear
Leaving only destruction -
Flooded lands, beaten unopened blossoms,
For the warmth of the Sun
And the love of the Earth, to heal.

A PLEASANT THOUGHT   Anna-Mary Howe

I like to hear a pleasant word
Soft spoken now and then,
I like to hear of something fine
That's happened to a friend.

I like to hear of happy thoughts
Or kind deeds being done.
I like it when the day is through
And new friends have been won.

I like to know that I have been
The cause of just some good,
That I've not lost a single chance
To help out when I could.

SNOW   Stanley E. Kukuk

From where you come I cannot tell,
But I can see where you shall dwell.

Shall in a phantom castle reign
Upon the frosted window pane,
Shall govern over all the land
That is the winter wonderland,
Shall cover trees with coats so fine,
As if to make for her a shrine,
Shall cover over hill and plain
Till utmost perfection attain.

When springtime breaks your magic spell,
A sense of loss I cannot quell.

DIES IRAE   Earle Griffin

Out of the sobbing of the rivers,
Out of the weeping of the rain,
Out of the vibrant groans of thunder
Shaking the valley and the plain,

Out of the lashing of the breakers,
Out of the ocean's heave and sigh,
Out of the festered streaks of lightning
Cutting the wrinkles across the sky,

Out of the throbbing of the marshes,
Out of the quiver of every clod,
I am aware of the infinite anguish
Borne of the grief of God.

A POET'S LIFE   Mildred Ezo

The poet's quest is life;
His mission not to gain
For with his poems he earns
All glory and all fame.

His theme is that of life
For that is what he lives;
And in the cheer he brings
Is paid back all he gives.

His gift to man is life
From deep down in his heart,
And in every poem he writes
This feeling is always a part.

AN OLD MAN'S THOUGHTS   John Wempe

I hear outside the sounds of living, that go on every day,
I hear the farmer in his field, busy making hay,
I hear the housewife in her home, working at her chore,
While I can only sit and wait, and sit and wait some more.

But it is my lot to sit inside, and strain my welcome ear,
To hear the sounds of cherished youth, the youth that seems so near,
For I have grown quite old, they say, four score years and nine,
And my lot is to sit alone, sit alone and pine.

THE LOST LIGHT   Barbara Gariepy

My sky is full of stars.
Which is my own? One shines brighter than the rest.
My feet are not firm.
I cannot reach it.

If I could see my star,
Then wresting it from heav'n would not be difficult.
Youth is my blindfold.
I cannot see it.

My eyes upon a star,
The disappointments of today could be forgot.
The roads lead elsewhere.
I cannot find it.

DEFINITION   Faye Harelson

The rain upon my roof,
    The wind that sings in tops of trees,
The blue of desert skies,
    The color of the falling leaves,
Are Poetry.

The things I see about me
    That come into my life,
The pleasure and serenity,
    The struggle and the strife,
Are Poetry.

The birds, whose songs
    Bring warmth and cheer,
The mountains and the valleys,
    And things that I hold dear,
Are Poetry.

SHADOWS AT SUNSET   Joy Evans

Slowly sets the western sun
Casting brilliant shadows o'er the land,
O'er mountains wrapped in purple cloaks
'Round a lucid lake and silver sand.

Shadows play majestic parts,
Mosses jade, mysterious emeralds at ease;
Cooing doves like lovers' words,
Sing their part in Nature's symphony.

RECOVERY   Wayne Smith

The winter has been long and dry.
The sand is piled on the fence rows.
It seems that even the pale, blue sky
Has forgotten how to rain and never shows
A single cloud that might try
To spread the moisture which everyone knows
Is so necessary on this prairie. Then, high
In the sky a cloud appears
Closer and closer it comes,
And despite everyone's fears,
Thunder sounds like approaching drums.
Then the sound which everyone hears
That means the world is green again,
And the heavens have once more been good to man.

A DREAM   Marilyn Boyd

A dream may be a faith to lean
Upon, a wish for higher things.
It may be inspiration seen
Awaiting revelation's wings.
A dream may be a frightening one -
Mysterious, thrilling like a ghost.
Though tense we lie till this dream's done,
We think of it as fun at most.
A dream is thinking, many times --
If more would only seek its good.
The ladder the creator climbs,
Close in our reach has always stood.
For dreams thought out and carefully planned,
In minds of men will ever stand.

GROWTH   Joanne Silver

A seed, a spade, a mound of rich black soil;
The sun, the rain, a wealth of living toil;
A shoot, a leaf, a bud of color gay;
The morn, the noon -- a flower to end the day.

ANTICIPATION   Martha Lee Legg

When winter's icy fingers grip your
          soul and heart,
You must not think of how your
          world has suddenly come apart,
But of the happy times you'll spend
          awaiting for the thing
That God and Nature have entitled:
          "The Coming of The Spring."

MY THANKS   Mary Kathleen Ervin

I thank You, God,
On this Thanksgiving Day
For the blessings I have
In every way.

The home where I live,
The food that I eat,
The clothes I wear,
And the friends I greet.

The school I attend,
Where democracy's taught,
And the hospital beds
Where the sick are brought.

The church where I worship
And learn about You,
And all the things
You'd have me do.

I pray for freedom
In our glorious land,
And the men who're fighting
That it might stand.

And last of all,
Dear God, I pray,
Thy helping hand
Along life's way.

REQUIEM TO AUTUMN   William E. Sauer

A requiem we sing to Autumn -
To see his technicolor mornings bestowing
Dewy tenderness upon the hardened earth.
The heat of the sultry summer is enveloped
In coolness as he throws back his naked trees
And from his mouth expels the winds
That bare the mind of thought.
An arrogant Autumn released from shrouded
Haunt, extends vast arms to set
The golden fields asway, and liberate
The beauty of the flower from its stem - to fade away.
Giving haste excuse that wither it must
As all do wither for even beauty has its time
Oblivious of its transience and impending doom
In this night without a moon,
For far above the clouded skies the glimmering
Stars foretell his fate while casting off
Their chilly glow. An undomesticated thief
Steals our tranquility and once more
Sends Autumn to his unimpassioned
Grave ... Slowly ties an icy robe around
Himself and lies down to his rest.

"SURF" - EXPRESSION   Francis V. McBride

The Surf, a rising melody,
        Surging through the air,
Serenades the siren moon,
        Unlistening - coldly fair;
Until, at last, the swirling strain
        Of Surf's star-spattered sweep
Slackens, like a drowsy child,
        And sings itself to sleep.

AMERICAN WORKERS   Evelyn Miyamoto

Men came from nations far and near
Of every race and every creed,
Men with open minds
To work and endure,
To live fully and be proud,
To die with their great task done
Of toiling and building
Their homes and a nation -
With justice and freedom for all.

MECHANICAL MEN — Loretta Georgi

I see mechanical men
wound and set
to go off
in one straight
and narrow path,
to look neither
to the left
nor to the right,
never back
always forward,
anticipating nothing -
accepting everything.

MY LADY'S MANTLE — Cecile Korte

My Lady's mantle of so quiet blue
Covers me with a softness not in the sky,
Colors my soul with oriental dye
That seeps into it, as each day comes new,
Too bright for eyes, too glorious a hue.
She sees my heart, my fear now, where I lie,
She heeds my constant, anxious, child-like cry,
With gentle patience. In the day, and through
The darkest fields of terrifying night
Where no paths go, she steps from deep to deep
Beside me to the brighter realms of peace
To that calm city where there is no need of light,
Where no dark comes, where is no need of sleep,
Where Christ is rest, and glory, and release.

TO A LILY — Mary Gallagher

O slender stem of gentle green
By tender leaves protected,
Thy gleaming cup imparts a sheen.
The hand of God directed.

O lily, pure and delicate,
Thy whiteness is untarnished.
As Mary, our sweet Advocate,
You take no part in carnage.

On high, to God Who is Most High,
The breeze your fragrance carries.
Your face has always faced the sky,
And there, like incense, tarries.

FLIGHT ACCOMPLISHED   Loretta Bogdan

They sent home wings that once you wore;
You do not need them anymore.
And when I look into the sky
I think of how you yearned to fly.

THE OUTCAST   Peter Bredehoeft

I am an American,
I was rejected in the House of the Lord
Whose foundation is laid on brotherhood of all men,
Yet I am an American.
I am looked down upon by many, and upheld by few,
Yet I am an American.
We fought side by side to save our nation,
Still I am rejected.
Why am I forced from the portals of learning,
Though I am an American?
I was cast out by rich, despised by poor.
Why am I driven from the path of life by others?
Still I'm an American.
Why am I different?
I'm the same as others,
Stature and build; blood and muscle,
Yet why am I discarded, cast away, downtrodden?
You may know,
For I am a Negro!

MOODS   Harriet Jones

Head high,
Shoulders back,
Stern face,
Steady pace,
          Pride.

Bright eyes,
Gay smile,
Sparkling talk,
Springy walk,
          Happiness.

Drooping shoulders,
Head low,
Dark eyes,
Heavy sighs,
          Discouragement.

ONLY MUSIC   Carol Collier

God, take away the necessary bread,
And take the lovely flowers from the hill;
Deny me all the sunset's gold and red;
Subtract these things, and I'll be happy still
If only You will leave the robin's song,
The voices, and the orchestras divine;
God, grant me wond'rous music all life long,
And all the world -- in music -- will be mine.

THE WILLOWY SIGHT   Janice Pinney

The willowy sight that meets my gaze
As the sun cuts a burning swath
Across the bare and swirling haze
Of truth bewildered and mayhap lost.

Belated inquiry, this fatal quest
Belie the innocence set as goal,
As the milling hundreds assume rest
With only self-pity, a deceptive shoal.

Tears of hope shed by a perceptive few,
Is this the pathway to the yearned for light
From resounding fury far from true
To clarify the heavens, to ease the night.

FRIEND AND FOE   Yvonne Noble

I am the soft hand which soothes
    The tired brow.
I am the demon Malstrom, snuffing
    Out men's lives.
I kill, and yet I save -- for
    I am water.

I am the silver dream
    Of de Leon.
I am the cure for Midas'
    Lust for gold.
Achilles' strength, Ophelia's disaster -
    That am I.

I am the wine of the wanderer
    And of the poor.
Kings revere me, and even He asked
    For my balm.
Friend and foe, strong and weak am I - for
    I am water.

WORDS   Mary Frances Scanlon

O Words,
Ye garments rare
In which men clothe their thoughts
And show them to their fellowmen,
Be kind!

TWO CITIES   Philomena Galat

A city I see with roads so dingy,
People in it selfish and stingy;
Hatred fills the atmosphere,
Nothing is considered dear.

Another city now I see,
Folks are gay and carefree,
Love is cherished all around,
Hatred nowhere to be found.

MARRED BEAUTY   Carolyn Isley

There is
    black soot
    on the white snow
like the
    mark of dishonesty
    on a pure life.

There is
    tarnish green
    on the silver spoon
like the
    sad eyes
    of a once smiling face.

There is
    bloody war
    on the rolling earth
like the
    self destruction
    which comes of greed.

There is
    a dark cloud
    hiding the sun's bright rays
like the
    shadow of guilt
    hiding God from my eyes.

THE BEGINNING OF SPRING   Sue Ellen Harris

The rosebud shivers in her thin green coat,
And longs for a brighter day.
While the pussy willow, snug in her smart furs,
Comes gayly out to play.

SUN, MOON, AND STARS   Bobby Newsome

The sun is a golden wheat field,
The moon a purple moor,
The stars are beacon lights,
Which guide planes in their flights.

WINTER WIND   Mary Ella Symes

Blustery -
mysterious yet simple,
the howling of the winter wind
as it blows
across hills and plains.

Lordly -
as it bows branches low
and breaks off limbs
for a sacrifice.

Whispering -
it creeps around the house
and fills
all the unseen cracks.

Winter music -
now high, now low
like a great chorus
it rises and falls,
led by a great conductor
in the sky.

Oh winter wind,
you are so big
and I am so little;
yet I love you, because
noisy -
you will blow winter away
and spring
quiet -
will slip in.

TOO YOUNG   Sherry Kay Carr

They told me
It was not love;
They said
I would forget;
They say
I am too young
To know;
But still
I wonder.
Why can't I forget?
Is it really I am young?
Or is it
They are old?

MOTHER   Susan C. McClary

Above her grave a willow is in bloom.
It seems not long since she left this fair earth,
Since she last sat within this very room,
And then we could not realize her worth.
She used to make the birds above her sing;
Her kindness spread to all of those in need,
And still in our young ears her kind words ring,
But while she lived, to them we paid no heed.
From her a glow of warmth did always spread;
To all who knew of her she was a friend.
It seems so strange to us that she is dead,
How greatly upon her we did depend.
The willow weeps upon the one we love,
Upon our mother, who has gone above.

A CURIOUS CUSTOM   Kay Nolting

I'll keep a little cottage
Below the high hill's crest
Where all brown-eyed people
Can set them down to rest.

There shall be plenty of plates
And mugs to melt the chill
Of all brown-eyed people
Who happen up the hill.

Yes, it is a curious custom,
But all the good I know
Was taught me out of two brown-eyes
A long, long time ago.

WANDERLUST   Mary Ann Appleman

One breath of wind; one faint temptation;
The thistle of a dandelion pulls from its protected crust.
It glides in a lonely, aimless movement,
A movement of wanderlust.

NIGHT SCENE   Pat Shannon

The moon tints treetops silver
As a careless painter might,
And the stars flirt back at light bugs
Like a million girls
At night.

The phantom cricket singers
Hide their faces from the light,
While the field mice roam like dancers
On a ballroom floor
At night.

My ears seek out its magic -
Long remembrance of each sight
Fills my mind with how it must be,
For I cannot see
The night.

LIFE   Nancy Zellman

Life is an infant
Happily
Curious, unheeded by time.

Life is a child
Merrily
Going on its way.

Life is a youth,
Warily
Realizing the ways of the world.

Life is a woman,
Bravely
Bearing cares of the home.

Life is a man,
Wearily
Facing death as it comes.

LAMENT   Cynthia Rogers

Blind Fate!
His unsung song
Is now quite lost; his work
Left here undone. Why did you let
Him die?

IT MATTERS   Lewis Sullivan

It matters much where I was born,
And if I were born rich or poor,
Whether I feared the cold world's scorn,
Or walked in the pride of wealth secure.

It matters much how long I will stay,
In a world of sorrow, sin and care,
Whether I will stay or be called away,
Or live till my bones of flesh are bare.

But it matters little where my grave is,
Whether on land or in the sea,
Or in beauty or in weeds,
It matters little or none to me.

Margaret Carmichael

I would be free!
Running
Jumping
Walking
Unfettered by cares and burdens,
Unsuppressed by doubts and fears.
I would be free!

I would be free!
Joyful
Happy
Carefree
Ready to face each new day and drain
Each new adventure of life to the dregs.
I would be free!

I would be free!
Roaming
Wandering
Seeking
Evermore the hidden secrets
Of life's forbidden mysteries. For this
I would be free!

YOUTH   Cecile Doyle

Youth, for all its vibrancy,
Is but a fleeting fancy.
Here today, gone tomorrow;
Something which the old would like to borrow,
But to the young it brings but pain,
With the longing for maturity,
And that which youth does not give,
That feeling of deep security.
Youth is but an act, a scene in the great play of life,
That scene of learning, yearning, and strife.

HIGHWAY SENTINELS   Diane Smith

As I walk along the highway
Giant claws reach out at me
Snarled and grasping branches
Of an old apple tree.

Autumn claimed their cloaks of velvet
Green with ruby-red
Spring brings a bright new mantle
To the trees asleep not dead.

THE LANE   Mildred Moffett

Nature's beauty is a simple thing
When you are living you're a king,
        You laugh, You cry,
        You love, You die.
But there's one thing that shall be
                forever maintained
That's nature's winding, rolling lane.

Winding here and winding there,
It doesn't have a worry or care,
Rolling forever in life's great span
Forever moving as a man

It keeps changing, dawn till night
It's really a beautiful and wonderful
                sight.
So to go on with my story until it ends
It will live longer than men.

HAPPINESS COMES   Sonne Hooper

Silent as an eagle floating on his way,
Quick as a hawk diving for the prey,
Lovely as the sun at the dawn of day,
Happiness comes.

Just as the air is stillest before a coming storm,
Just as night is darkest before the daylight warm,
So is sorrow hardest to bear, just before
Happiness comes.

MUSIC   Berlyn Nishimura

Music of beauty and grace lingers
Permanently;
Like the continuous waves dashing and rolling
Endlessly;
Like my moods, its divergent notes are always
Changing;
Like my mind, capacity and depth in tones are valued
Sublimely;
Like my character, enrichment towards perfection is desired
Continually;
Like my soul, it needs appreciation
Constantly;
Music of such grace and beauty shall be in my heart
Eternally.

A SONNET ON AUTUMN   Diane Beck

'Tis Autumn with her colors bright and fair
There's almost every hue - green, brown and gold.
It seems she splashes them 'most everywhere.
Some of them warm, and others are so cold.
The trees, their leaves to Mother Nature throw.
The birds go South in search of better food.
The days are growing shorter now, it seems.
All things blend into such a pleasant mood.
The rain, the frost, the dew. Oh! How it gleams!
The people busy as the leaves they rake.
The moon so pretty and the sun with beams.
Oh! Such a magic spell one cannot break.
This is my favorite season of the year
When Mother Nature sends us Heaven down here.

SUMMER STORM   Pat Lochard

Great, round, raindrops plunking down
Cooling off the dusty ground.
Lightning lacing through the sky
The ground folk laugh, when the heavens cry.

ADVENTURE OF A ZEPHYR   Viola Fuehr

A gentle zephyr played among the bright
Crisp, falling, colored autumn leaves and boughs.
And then it dashed to tease some near-by cows.
It did such naughty things with great delight.

And then it thought it might be fun to fight
A hawk but found out how this bird endows
Its strength upon its victim; so with bows
It left in quite capitulating fright.

But now the wind has had enough of those
Unruly acts; so an amenity
Was now performed in place of shameful deeds.
It now skipped shyly to a sleeping rose
And chased from that sweet sleeping face a bee.
And then it disappeared around some tall green reeds.

REFLECTION   Maryliz Milling

Which trees are more real:
The trees God did make,
Or the black silhouettes
In the depths of the lake?
Which sky has more stars:
The sky overhead,
Or the sky nestled deep
In the lakes muddy bed?
Which moon shines more brightly:
The moon in the sky,
Or the moon down below,
Where the fish, sleeping, lie?

One night is the stiller:
The night on the hill;
For the night in the lake
Is a quivering still.

SUNSET   Peggy Sias

The colors stretch across the sky against the fading blue;
A tall and lonely, scrawny pine pierces the brilliant hue;
The red sun sinks behind the wall of blackening forest trees,
And sends its last short mellow rays upon the wondrous frieze;
The clouds of red and gold and orange streak out across the sky,
And as I watch, they fade away and, till tomorrow, die.

THE MORNING SUN   Nancy Sommerville

Pink as the flush of a lover's cheek
Oh morning sun, arise!
Stretch your arms over hill and dale,
Open sleepy eyes.
Paint the sky with a "Master hand"
And leave a rainbow trail.

THE LONESOME PINE   Don C. Leo

The lonesome pine,
As time goes by,
Stands up above
With watchful eye.

It sees the folk
Go by below
In summer heat
And winter snow.

Its graceful bend
That wind did cause,
Is seen in snow
And springtime thaws.

The mountains that
It tow'rs above
Are too far away
To show it love.

And so it stands,
That lonesome tree,
Above the world
For all to see.

A REFLECTION   Barbara Selby

Now as I sit in the bustling classroom, I wonder --
I wonder if I shall miss the restless students
Anxiously counting the minutes on the old, battered clock.
I wonder what they'll be in a few years --
Perhaps millionaires, glorying in their elaborate surroundings,
Oblivious of common discomforts,
Secure in their luxury.
Perhaps teachers, like this one - stern, commanding,
And yet (I suppose) secretly remembering when he, too, was
Wondering.

BEAUTY OF LIFE   Diane Moren

When life seems like a long and boring book,
And troubles crowd your mind throughout each day,
Then wander down beside the rushing brook
And let its waters wash your cares away.
And if your brow is dark and deeply-lined,
If age has told its weary tale too soon,
Then go into the springtime air and find
The freshness of the flowers now in bloom.
When even loved ones disappear from sight,
Or friendship that you've cherished slowly dies,
Then gaze into the peaceful stars at night;
Return the smile that warms the friendly skies.
The beauty nature placed upon the earth
Can soothe your pain and show you life's true worth.

MAN'S PROGRESS   Cecelia Cox

Our age of miracles has come to us,
Now man can span the skies on silver wings.
He rides in comforts once thought fabulous,
But now to him most ordinary things.
From spear, to lance, to gun, to deadly atom,
The instruments of war were altered too.
For man in war's wild pandemonium
No wrong, no shame, he will not dare to do.

For while commanding nature's wondrous powers
Yet man would waste the force of eons for death.
The power to build, the gifts that might be ours
Are drained by man for taking life's sweet breath.
Will man forever more use strength for ill
And sharpen wits so precious blood can spill?

THE GLADE   Beau Kansteiner

The green glade where we dreamed the days away
        Has been swallowed by the city.
Where once our willow cabin stood
        There's a mountain of tin cans.
But, I'll always remember ----
The green of the trees, the smell of the young river.
The stream seems to sing out of the past
Swirling the taste of fresh, cold spring water to me.
Though time may try to change it,
She can never really win.

THE WHEELLESS CART   Bob Parris

The man who has no song in his heart
Might be likened to a wheelless cart.
If a man will not release his soul,
He is like the cart that cannot roll.

What can I do? Why, look at Poe!
High as the angels, yet, oh, so low!
We who are lowly might sing quite the same,
In those limitless heights which no one can name.

VALUES   Boyce Major

A house is made of many things,
Metal, wood and stone;
But friendship's ties are made of love -
Love which comes from God alone.

Stone and metal have their age,
However lasting they may be.
The love that dwells in human hearts
Grows and lives eternally.

You may live in an intellectual realm,
And yet your life be spent in vain,
For if no neighbor is there to help,
What good is a genius's brain?

A house of wood may soon decay,
And yet you know 'tis true,
Although the heart may turn to dust,
Love glows and flames anew.

NEARING THE END   Jere Thompson

I'm wending my way along a road
And, Oh, so heavy is my load.
It's leading me up a grade so steep,
That often I fall just like a sheep.

Oh, what is the goal when I reach the top?
Or does the learning ever stop?
This question often in my mind I ponder,
As daily along this trail I wander.

We learn so much, and forget even more,
But learning is never a useless chore.
For each bit of knowledge we strive to gain
Will help us the goal, at last, to attain!

A DREAMER'S HOME   Eugene Sage

The wind, the sea, an island for a town;
A bay, white sands, and rocks would be the yard;
Blue corals, yellow green and red around
Would be a natural garden quite unmarred.
The house would be of hand-shaped twigs and twine;
Thatched ceiling, sides, dirt floor - the native touch.
Green foliage, palms, in back no boundary line
To bar and block the owner from so much.
Far back and up the handmade house would lie;
A large and yet protected clearing there
For me to look out over sea and sky,
To sit and dream with long and vacant stare ...
To have this home I'd need no yearly lease,
For here the days, and time itself, would cease.

JEWELS   Doris Burns

Tiny drops of heartbreak,
Liquid dynamite,
Shimmering bits of sadness,
Morning, noon, or night

Bittersweet and sparkling,
As the rainbow hues,
Priceless, yes, and urgent,
As an actor's cues,

Touching, sad, endearing
Throughout all the years
Unexplainable, reminiscent,
These are human tears.

WAR   Carol Olson

War, crashing, thundering, booming
Destruction, heartbreak, death following in its wake.
Man against man, brother against brother,
Truth against lies, love against hatred,
Brotherhood against greed, power against weakness,
Is this what we shall know?
Is this the atmosphere in which our children shall grow up?
Or will we, God's children,
Settle our grievances
And live in love and peace with our brothers in God?

LIFE   Bruce Burns

Night of chaos into morn;
Morn of love into the noon;
Noon of strife into the night.
It is gone, to return no more.
But now it is ours, ours;
For we created the havoc hours.
The day was our puppet then
But now in death we follow it.
For we are the puppet of our life.

ELEGY   Sharon King

Oh ghastly pallid face so chalky white
Whose dim and faded eyes that shine no more,
Are eyes as hard and dull as vulcanite,
Whose heart is like the rotted apple core.

No mask could be as fixed as your face,
All life and living things drained from your soul,
A death-like body left without a trace
Of love nor beauty that I used to know.

I wish that I could kiss you once again,
And hear your soft voice sweetly calling me;
For speaking words of wisdom you said then,
To watch my step upon this troubled sea.

But now my steps are faltering from fear
For I am lost and left with just a tear.

TEARS OF LIFE Jerry Segroves

I walk the dark, lonely path of life,
As a lone shepherd at night --
Watching through both wind and rain;
As I walk on, and on, and on.

I sail the unresting seas of life,
A captain at the wheel of his ship --
Through both storms and strife;
I sail on, and on, and on.

I come at last to the end of my journeys,
To stand before my God --
My judgment comes; at last I sleep
In peace, forevermore.

TRANSFORMATION   Nancy Seidel

Through the day it's just a tree,
A haven for birds, flying free.
A protection for a house from the noon-day light,
A place for squirrels to return to at night.

Then as the sun goes to its rest,
And the clouds turn purple in the west,
The tree takes on a grander air,
A thing of beauty, inviting prayer.

At the top, the twigs so delicate,
Are tinged with the gold only God can create.
While the tree emerges a glorious gold lace,
A purple altar of God to grace.

SPRING SYMPHONY   Jane Spaeth

Hear the rippling of each stream,
As it plays its welcome theme.
Hear the balmy breezes blow,
Where the pussy-willows grow.

Hark! the robins sweetly trill
In the trees upon the hill.
Hark! the buzzing of the bee
Adds its little song of glee.

Listen in the dusk descending
To the peepers' voices blending.
Listen! Who would not agree?
This is spring's sweet symphony!

CHARACTER   John Kunzmann

Build it well, what you try to do;
Build it erect and good and true;
Build it clear, clean and broad;
Build it worth the eye of God;

Build it now, whoever you are;
Build it for the judgment hour;
Build it now, for on that day,
Your character will be there to stay.

A CUT GLASS VASE   Lonnie Fisk

You capture sunlit rays of gold,
And lure them to your web-like fold
Of mystic beauty glistening fair,
Among your crystal cuts most rare.

Diffused reds and blues become shimmering purple,
When shone on your countenance gaily encircled.

You stand as you are, a cold, hard vase,
But the sun warms your heart with its glittering rays.

THE WORDS IN TIME   Gerry Haskins

If moments were not fleeting,
So much you now could say
To make this hour brighter -
To change the night to day.

But moments are still passing -
Each minute and each hour.
Need I say more to tell you
I need your strengthening power?

Power filled, those strengthening words
Put to rest thy haunting past;
They wake the sleeping morn
And rest thee then at last.

Last, not least, to say this much,
As time goes passing on,
Each moment in each hour
Will bring a bright new dawn.

HEAVEN   Jean Larcom

Heaven is the vineyard of the heart men
       set aside,
And plant with memories of joy and love.
And as the Time of Harvesting draws nigh,
The fruit is pressed, and all the waste
       removed,
Leaving the purest nectar of the soul.

SPEAK, YOUNG MAN   Fred Krueger, Jr.

Speak up, young man;
Speak up for democracy.
For the way of life you've enjoyed,
Since first rock of cradle.
Speak. Say what you may
Before that privilege is taken away.
It's talk -- free talk,
You've taken for granted,
As orators raved and
Politicians have ranted.
Speak up, youth. Look to the world.
Say what you mean.
And mean what you say.
Freedom of Speech, forever,
In the traditional American way!

THE SKY AT NIGHT   Barbara Burroughs

Folds of jet black velvet,
   A great big glowing moon,
A million shining stars above,
   Like diamonds on a blue lagoon.

The milky way is pouring --
   A glass for you and me,
And stars are falling here and there,
   Off heaven's shining tree.

A symphony is playing,
   The music sweet and clear,
And everything turns silent,
   And seems to lend an ear.

An endless plain of space,
   Around this little globe,
As night so softly takes
   The world into its robe

WATER LILY   Lois Ann Gross

Sweet flower, so charming, so chaste, so serene,
Bobbing gently up and floating down the stream.
How does it feel to rock in the rippling swells,
To loll in the sunshine and sail through the dells?

You are a throne for the mightiest of frogs,
Out in the middle of musty old bogs.
You are a rose in the waters of time,
You are the object of this little rhyme.

So, sail on, sail on, forever in peace,
And may your sweet loveliness never cease.

MAKE BELIEVE   Anna Lee Morgan

Make believe the rocks could talk
And the flowers and the trees could sing
And the birds and the fairies walk
On the threads of beautiful spring.

Make believe that the brooklet would stop
And so would the wind on the lee;
And the grasshoppers would no longer hop.
What then would this world of ours be?

BIRTH AND DEATH OF A ROSE
Jo Anne Kok

A newborn rose begins to bloom
    Its fragrant smell ascending,
With silken petals open wide
    And colors softly blending.

Already dew has washed its face
    And added to its splendor,
And now the sun upon it shines
    A smile so warm and tender.

But alas, a storm has come
    And unmindful of this flower,
Sends its torrents lashing through
    With all its might and power.

Thus ends the rose's gentle life
    Its death was brief and snappy,
But even though it was so short
    Its life was very happy.

AUTUMN SILENCE   Wilma Jean Blosser

The breathless moments of an autumn day
Prove summer seems to linger, almost stay.
The winds blow quietly o'er the fields of yellow grain
And the tall, sweetly scented pines after a rain;
The sweetest things on earth are quiet things,
That hushed suspense before the small bird sings.

A WOODLAND PATH   Jacquelyn Stevens

Dancing moonbeams
Shadowed blue and silver on the woodland path
Lined by ghost-like trees
With reaching arms
Silhouetted by the midnight moon,
Deserted like a haunted house
As lonely as a mummy's tomb;
Among gloomy evergreens dark as the blackness of night
Shine flashing, piercing eyes
Of forest creatures.
Rustling sounds disturb the unbroken silence
As a sudden wind stirs the still of night.

AMERICA   Shirley McVicar

America is a beautiful poem,
Building verse by verse,
Composed from the imagination
Of its people.

Its rhythm ... the hum of
                great machines,
The pulsing of city traffic,
The swaying of native trees.

Its rhyme ... the singing of
                mountain rills,
The bantering of corner
                hawkers,
The symphony of great construction.

Its theme ... the recollection of
                great conquests,
The thrill of bygone adventures,
The satisfaction of dreams
                fulfilled.

I AM A POET   Mary Oliver

I sing of new creations,
And of old, ancient things,
I find beauty in all, and share it
              with the world.
My heart sings with the joy
              of life and living,
Or plunges to the depths
              of desolation.
In me is the power to create.
I am a poet.

PEACE   Donna Goodison

Peace, thou art a maid, beautiful and fair.
Thy face is fine; thy eyes as bright as stars.
Thy robes are rich, and jewels crown thy hair.
No imperfections can thy beauty mar.

Men seek you, and would have you, but you flee.
You are elusive and remain to bless but few,
And few there are who will your partners be,
For your colleagues must in their thoughts be true.

You dwell not in a city or a town,
But in the hearts of those who love you well.
Wherever you are, you spread your joy around,
And happy homes will of your presence tell.

As long as I know you are in men's hearts,
I shall not despair nor with my courage part.

EVENING'S CALL   Patricia Ann Preston

Twilight sits upon the world;
Heavy, silent, breathes the air;
Flaming red with sparks of gold,
The lord of the western sky bows low.

Slowly homeward wend their way
Man and beast of the weary earth;
Night with soothing calmness spreads
Peace and balm on aching hearts.

Somewhere in the distance, chimes
Call the thoughts of all to Him,
Maker of this glorious land,
Help and strength to all in need.

A LIGHT   Bob Nelson

In the distance thunder's great voice roars
   And we see a flash from where an eagle soars
      These brilliant sparks of light to earth must fall
         Then, as if in answer, there comes Old Thunder's call.
The jagged cutlass that strikes out, up in the sky
   Canst but be wielded by the Maker in gloryhigh
      Is it a sign, O'Father, who has made this light
        Is it a warning of your wrath and might?

DECEMBER AT DUSK   Linda Stern

A mist of white hangs in the air,
A frosty veil for Winter's hair.
Resplendent in her gown of snow,
December feels the cold winds blow
And bluster while the light of day
With sunset dies and fades away.

Now evening flings her silver stars
Across the sky, and from afar
A church bell ringing Christmas cheer
Is heard. The moon's great silver sphere,
In solemn, slow, majestic flight,
Soon fills the world with holy light.

OUR PRAYER   Deborah Boggin

Shadows and light play dimly on
Long after we are dead and gone.
Will the black and white of war and peace
Beat ever on, and never cease?

Like the chessboard's mighty war
The guns of battle boom and roar.
While mothers pray and sweethearts weep,
Unknowing children lie asleep.

Unceasingly the long distress
Among mankind must be redressed.
But who can say when war will stop
So man his deadly tools may drop?

Time flies away, and we may see
Our sons at war on land and sea.
Lord, God, we turn for help to Thee
Pray, grant us peace eternally.

WINGS   Bettie Thomas

I came upon a field
With dandelions gay.
It burst into the air with song,
A flock of birds in May.

Today I saw the ocean
With waves of snowy white.
I gave these waves a pair of wings
And a seagull rose in flight.

THE ALARM CLOCK   Gretchen Fuller

What an impolite old thing,
Equipped with that darn bell to ring.
Just when a good dream's at its peak,
It sounds off with an awful shriek.
Then not content with what it has done,
Faster and faster its black hands run,
Stressing the fact that time is going to waste,
And there soon will be need to make great haste.
It's made of steel; its heart's a spring.
It would think life a horrid thing,
If it were the one that had to rise,
So soon in the morning to open its eyes,
To hurry without any time to fool,
To get up, get ready, and go to school.

SONNET TO A SONG   Lois Dale

Your melody comes floating rich and sweet,
First haunting mind, then capturing our hearts,
Expressing not with words, but rhythmic beat
The joy you feel, the love your soul imparts.
O, Song, have you a soul, or have you not?
From where could such a mighty feeling flow
If not from out some hidden inmost spot
Which only God unlocks and lets you go.

O, lovely song, that we could be like you,
And let from out each lonely heart appear
A love and gladness ever rich and true
To help rebuild a world so torn with fear.
But just as you can never be like me,
I'll never make myself as pure as thee.

TIME AND TRADITION Donna Ann Johnson

I say, sir, can you tell me of the time?
I know the hour is late --
Nay? Then 'tis a shameful crime I've done!
Sir, all great deeds are done by clockwork,
A country saved, one conquered, too -
And how could our great leaders carry through
Each plan of patriotism true
Without this influental element? What's more,
What would the consequences be?
Consider, sir, for 'tis of great concern to me --
I must have my tea at four.

PRACTICING Marie Hudson

He takes out his Trumpet and lifts it high.
He holds it; he fondles it; he acts like a genius.
He lifts it to his lips and draws a long breath
And out comes this --- Bloop! Sharp Bloop!
              Flat Bloop!
And then a long, Wavering Bloop that trails off
                      into agonized silence
That was "Taps!"
That sound should have discouraged him.
Did it?
Bloop! Bloop! Sharp Bloop! Flat Bloop!
Oh ---- No ---- !

FUNERAL OF AUTUMN LEAVES
                      Marilyn Burkhart

The year is slowly dying
    as the leaves their brightness shed
To assume the dull brown cloak
    of the dying or the dead.

The leaves are all in mourning
    as to their death they fly,
They'll never see again
    the beauty of the sky.

The funeral now is past.
    the leaves lie 'neath the snow
To give the earth new life
    but not again to grow.

SHADOWS   Elaine Sampson

A crown of sweat adorns his brow
His sinewy muscles are bands of steel
Which ripple on a darkening sea
Wherein the ebon of his skin
Presses an ever-teasing stain
Which wounds our Lord and names man equal.

NOLI TIMERE   Leo Fitzpatrick

When at length thou tread'st the other shore,
And troubles of this wretched life retreat,
The sod, however firm beneath thy feet,
May give thee cause to doubt its firmness more:
When Life's laborious task is o'er,
It seems to mortal vision incomplete,
If all thy friends thou dost not chance to meet.
Despair not! Joy is thine forevermore!
Not all thy friends by thousands multiplied,
Their hearts outpouring all their finite love,
Can e'er compare with Him Whose glorified
Possession o'ershadows all mortal love.
He with Whom forever thou wilt abide,
Shall be thy rest, thy joy, thy peace, thy love.

TELL ME   Gail Gray

How many GI's have asked of us
"Just what are we fighting for?"
How many dead in Korean fields
Knew the purpose of this war?

How many parents waiting here
Know why their sons must suffer?
How many statesmen groping here
Guess what victory might offer?

How many in those deadly hills
Know why we fight for others?
What lad would tell you over there
"We're fighting 'cause we're brothers.

How many know that peace must be
For all - or not for any?
The boys are learning over there
But over here - how many?

AUTUMN PATTERNS   Lee McClement

Dreamily through auburn leaves
Lazy golden light is gleaming
Something breaks the patterned glow:
A blue jay's flight and startled screaming.

Crisp crackling of dry leaves
Beneath my dusty shoes
Burnt sienna, golden, scarlet -
All the flaming hues.
A tawny woven tweed, with shades
That richly blend and fuse.

WIND   Conrad Hoffman

When the wind blows and its cutting fingers
      seem to clutch the human life
            into a senseless emotion;

It pushes along the clouds and reaches
      down to lift high the waves
            of the ocean;

'Tis then as it blows across the earth
      all life seems to bow
            before its motion.

BOGUS BATTLEGROUND   Mary Steel Clark

Each droplet is a tiny man,
Armed in coat of mail,
That shimmers as it hits the earth,
In garden or on trail.

The rich soil is their battleground,
Their stations are the roots;
Sunshine's rays their weapons forge,
And tempers shining suits

Remember dear old Auntie's phlox,
The ones you trampled down?
Those were the turret stations tall;
The posts of a pigmy town.

NOISE   Martha Jane Singeltary

Voices outside,
Cars in the rain,
A lonesome train whistle,
A melancholy strain.
A blaring radio,
A cry of joy,
A happy song,
The clatter of a heavy toy.
A peaceful laugh,
A sharp call,
A teacher's voice
Far down the hall.

THE HANDS OF TIME   David Byrn

If I could make the hands of time stand still
As one can stop a movie camera scene
Or pull the wall plug of a clock at will,
I think I'd choose a time most unforeseen.
For that is when the good sometimes shows traits
Impure and evil to the very core,
And when a man who low in goodness rates
Might add a little stock to kindness' store.
The good are good, the bad are bad, they say;
And thus we classify the kinds of men.
If we could follow just one life some way,
We'd see it's hard to choose the saints from sin.
I think a thousand books of life I'd fill
If I could make the hands of time stand still.

A HEAVENLY PLIGHT   Donna Yates

At an angel's tears Saint Peter sighs,
And then he stops and wonders why.
A Cosmic Being such as she
Upset as this should never be.
It seems this little angelic one
Was one day having some heavenly fun,
And forgetting she was a perfect being.

She lost her halo and now is grieving.
Ah, but Saint Peter thinks he knows
How to get rid of this angel's woes.
For if she's good and does what's right,
He'll have it back in time for tonight.

WISHES   Helen Sharp

Star -- of
All the people
Who have wished on
You tonight, will many have wished
In vain?

HOPE   Rahuel Westrup

Stars in darkness, stars aglow
                in heaven's almighty domain,
In thine unheeded course thou hast seen
Serfdom and darkness from some do abstain
While others ignorance and toil their lot has been.
Thou hath gazed upon an earth of suffering and turmoil;
Hate and detesting in its path hath brought
And no wonder; strife, rivalry, and cruelty in it boil
Wickedness that reasoning men have wrought.
Yet in its depth a light of hope doth gleam;
To those who shelter from evil seek it beckons.
Peace and eternal life to all gives its beam,
But those whom darkness seek with their Maker reckon.
Oh heavenly bodies, in it thou seest
                salvation come in slow gait,
And iniquity blown away by trust and faith!

THE WIND   Patricia Scully

In reverent awe the trees all round
Do bend and curtsey toward the ground.
The buttercup in meadows green,
Of nature's jewels, no doubt the queen,
Its fealty does show profound.

And every little bud and mound
Is trembling with approaching sound,
And waiting - can they all be seen
In reverent awe.

Then comes the monarch with a bound,
His place among his subjects found.
They glitter with an outdoor sheen;
But he alone can not be seen,
Although by these he has been crowned
In reverent awe.

A MELODY   Kay Kellough

A melody like a costly gem
I find when not expecting wealth -
A strain most often glad, but sometimes sad,
That awakens a love heart-felt.

A note that speaks when I cannot -
A word of wisdom in a tune -
Music, as old as God, as old as all,
A melody tht lights the world for me.

A FELINE   Katherine Blackwell "Trina" Twyeffort

A cat is a feline, half pixie, half fur,
The soul of a devil lies under her purr.
A secret lurks deep in the eyes of a cat
As she stares into space while stretched out on her mat.
The paws of a feline are cushions until
From out them stretch weapons for pounce and for kill.
The tail of a pussy may writhe like a snake,
But can bristle and swell to make men and mice quake!
A pussy cat sits by the fire, a queen.
As tigress, stalks jungles when dusk forms a screen.
One moment a cat rolls a ball on the ground,
The next, on stiff legs she whirls madly around.
For cats are all pixies, quite covered with fur,
And souls of red devils hide under their purr!

BASEBALL CROWD   Jackie Baggett

They are a motley bunch,
The crowd -
Some are eating their lunch,
The crowd -
Rolled up shirt sleeves, emotions showing,
Screaming, yelling, hissing, booing,
The crowd -
The ump (the roach), the players, the coach,
None are exempt. They show no mercy,
The crowd -
The flash of spikes, the sudden stillness,
Some are even brought to illness,
But they'll be back for more.
The crowd -

THOUGHTS   Nancy Hull

My thoughts
Like small children,
Run in fascination
And bewilderment through the maze
Of Life.

A CHERUB'S FANCY   Patricia Finnegan

A cherub's dream imbibed a stately jaunt
Through fairyland, its marvels to explore.
The queerness of its wonders failed to daunt
Her quiet joy, for here would end her chore.

She'd traveled o'er the planets, though, in vain
To meet some friend who would imposing be.
She thought a king must guide this quaint domain
And furnish luster for its royal glee.

Ahead she saw an opal-colored stone.
A reindeer pointed out a regal tree.
A teddybear reclined upon a throne,
Enraptured by the snowmen's Christmas spree.

She smiled at him through snowy branches green;
He begged her hand, and she became his queen.

WILLOW   Mary Bolander

Willow, willow, bending low,
Do you fear the breezes so,
When like lashing blasts they blow?

When like teasing breath they flow
Through your branches, soft and low,
Do you then bend down so low?

Willow, I would like to know,
Since you're near me, down so low,
Would you stop to say hello?

Could you on the mountain grow,
In some valley be for show,
Is your head in shame bowed low?

A good lesson you bestow,
On us folk who meet with woe,
You can't break while bending low.

IDEAS IN SOUND — Kenneth Castek

From a slowly revolving black mirror
A stylus transmits thought images from between
The sides of a spiral groove; the hearer
Receives impressions from one unseen.

Sounds from lips now still
Shall enlighten many; shall last
Beyond their time! Engraved images will
Ignore death; time's sonic barrier is past.

REMEMBRANCE — Bob Morrell

When cold and bleak the winds from Northland blow
And blanket all the land in freezing white,
For some - a mystic land, when comes the snow -
For me - a deathly still land greets my sight.

A ghostly form where once a spruce tree grew,
A leering monster transformed from a car;
Where overhead a singing bird once flew -
A canopy of clouds hides every star.

When I recall the pleasant days of June -
The fragrance of the air that comes from rain -
Then Summer like a softly humming tune
Returns to cast its spell o'er me again.

But, surely as the blossom from bud grows,
The Spring again will burst forth from the snows.

HE WHO SINGS PRAYS TWICE — Catherine Offringa

Soothing, gentle music
Slowly fills the air,
The choir sings like angels
Standing white-robed there.
Hymns of praise to God
Floating towards the sky,
Carried up by angels
To the throne on high.
Heart and soul pour forth
To making notes precise,
No truer words were spoken than:
He who sings prays twice!

DEATH   Shiela Molyneux

When Death's whisper comes
Soft and silent at the ebbing time of life,
When darkness seems to cover all --
Our hopes, our dreams, our fears,
Why sorrow then for earthly things?
This is not death, but birth
        Unto eternity!

NIGHT   Joanne Agard

Here I sit alone, the walls resounding nothing,
Being born of stone and plaster.

As I sit I gaze in a speechless wonderment
Of you, oh dark and villainous night!

As I watch you slither over the horizon
You stretch out your enormous arms,

And cloak this meager civilization
Into an endless and empty blackness.

You sullenly cradle us till day breaks,
Then gently and with a touch of sentiment

You recede slowly over the lusty snow-capped hills.

CRY OF THE FALCON   Karen Olson

Hark, listen to the call
The wind brings swifter.
Listen to the cry of eerie wing,
Silently floating overhead.

Not bound to man,
Now he flies free
His sharp eye waiting, watching,
No telltale sign he leaves.

On and on hovering nearer
Skimming through the empty space
Beak and claw ready are
Shined and sharpened naturally.

So beware quiet woodfolk
Of the killer of the skies
Silently, swiftly, descending
No sound uttered, no sound said.

AUTUMN RAIN   Marjorie Beck

Dead leaves flutter down,
Slitting mist's gray gown.
Rain pours in to fill the gaps
Between the clouds, into laps
Of woodland streams and pools.
Raindrops sparkle, untold jewels
Spilling out of open coffers.
To all the mourning world it offers
Unstifled sobs and cleansing tears
Through the sorrows of the years.

FAITH TODAY   William Emblidge, Jr.

If we have only one faith today,
If we have only one belief,
If that faith is not faith in God,
And that belief is not belief in love,
Then all is lost.
If that faith is the faith in God,
If that belief is belief in love,
If all pray to that faith
And all live that belief,
Then we have hope.

TRANSFORMATION   Margaret Spates

There is no sound of the organ's note,
No candle lights, no flowers.
The church, from door to door, is packed
As the priest begins Three Hours.
There is no joy or gladness now,
Some women sob aloud,
As the priest reads of Christ's Passion
And the jeering, mocking crowd.
Yet two days hence, the joyous notes
Of the organ fill the air.
The candles blaze, the altar blooms
With pure, white flowers there.
Each heart is filled with gladness,
Where sorrow once has been.
The statues are uncovered,
For Christ has ris'n again.

AUTUMN'S MYSTERY　　　　Margaret Van De Grift

The golden leaves of autumn fluttered
　　slowly to the ground,
They parted from the branches, and
　　then fell without a sound.
The earth was cloaked in browns and reds,
　　and trimmed with threads of gold,
Each leaf, an amber drop of wine
　　from cups that overflowed.
Bare branches waved a lofty cry
　　to autumn skies of blue,
And bowed before the coming winds
　　as loyal subjects do.

YOUTH'S PLEA FOR JUSTICE　　　　Beverly Daubert

Oh, why, must we, the youth that's of today,
Be so compelled to fight for all that's dear?
Why must we see life's cruel and bloody way
And live with such unhappiness and fear?
Oh, will there ever be that glorious time
When all who live can work and play as one;
And there will be that feeling so sublime,
When power means wholesome brotherhood and fun?

But not until the selfishness and greed
Can be completely banished from the earth.
And to the good of all we pay more heed,
Instead of just our individual worth.
For then the hope of universal peace,
Will be fulfilled, and all the wars shall cease.

LIBERTY　　　　Vicki Bloye

The earth or man himself long ages past
Molded the chains that made Oppression king,
Crowned Tyranny, and left mankind a thing
Abject. And still the tyrant's hold is fast.
Does man so love his chain, his binding thong?
Or does he see no hope, no way to break
The power that he can give but cannot take?
Strange how King Tyranny still rules so strong!
In quiet places, was but lately born
A little prince, usurper to the throne --
Liberty -- sworn to set earth's peoples free.
Young, insecure, oft-threatened, and forlorn,
Will he yet perish, latent strength unshown?
And will Oppression reign eternally?

FALL   John Farrant

Daylight dims with the frost,
Dark skies moan, "Summer's lost,"
Death blows hard on their souls,
"To die," Fall's death-bell tolls.
    Leaves among their brightness fall,
    Leaving death mats over all;
    Warm winds dash the garden's head,
    Summer's youth to Death is wed.
Curtsey leaves; branches bow!
Coldness keeps Winter's vow!

WAR   Ned C. Neibarger

Through bloodshot eyes,
The world he spies.
Its cut and battered head.

Its beauty dies
Beneath the skies,
The dark clouds overhead.

The blood lies red
On fields and bed
Of the heroes that are dead.

VIDERE   Katy Coopland

This morn as I awake to glorious dawn
My eyes behold the handiwork of God:
The sparkling drops of dew upon the lawn,
The wispy milkweed seeds from in the pod,
And many little pleasures; sights unseen
By eyes that search not for the precious gifts
His hand divine has giv'n. To me they mean
A myriad of loveliness. The rifts
Of jewelled waves upon a sandy shore
Are wont to stir my soul to wondrous dreams;
Each step I take brings sight of marvels more
To dwarf the shrewdest of man's crazy schemes.
Then God who pities me in searching plight
Brings twinkling stars, the heralds of peaceful night.

AUTUMN'S MAGIC — Martha Elizabeth Wade

Autumn is a suave and faithless lover,
Keeping his treachery undercover.
He woos the trees into Bright array,
Then like a thief steals their beauty away.
He flatters the flowers 'til their hearts are lost.
Then blights their loveliness with killing frost.
He paints the hills with sunset glow
Then covers them with an early snow.
He is the Pied Piper of harvest season;
Piping his magic without rhyme or reason.
Though the leaves know that to feel the touch of his breath,
That intoxicating fragrance will lead them to death.
When the shortening days announce him in fall,
All nature must answer his amorous call.

RESTLESS MEMORIES — Rita Miller

How can one blot out
The memories that come unasked,
Suddenly as tears,
Recurrent as the summer rains.
Here a fleeting glimpse of a face,
There, the fragment of a song,
Scented pine trees in the night.
Again the memories surge
Forming a kaleidoscope.
Is it possible to forget?

SNARED — Clare Coakley

The wind came lilting through the trees,
Dancing in aimless gaiety.
And the leaves in answer laughed in rustle,
And settled back in mockery.

The wind came running through the trees,
Bent on a definite goal.
But the leaves laughed again and soon settled
back
Content with the strength of their souls.

The wind came whistling through the trees,
Lashing like whips of steel,
And left in the gutter behind it the leaves
Helpless souls in a gale.

MIDNIGHT MISSION   Bonita Sue Drew

The buildings lie in the arms of the night,
Sleepy windows winking here and there.
Hidden tension in the movements of dark figures
Standing in the wind.
Quiet words, muffled noises,
Propellers turn with a rush of sound;
And they are gone.

THE APPRENTICE POET'S LAMENT   Lois Jean Nelson

Why can't I write as the masters do
    Express my joy and sorrow?
I guess that I shall only be
    A critic in the long tomorrow.

I wish that I could write my thoughts
    If only to a tree,
They may not be as good as some
    But at least I tried, you see.

Although I shall not be a success
    As now my poetry looks,
I shall never tire of verse and words
    As long as there are books.

THE SPRING AGAIN   Margaret Duggar

Soft springtime's space of residence
Full many signs foretell;
A vague excitement fills the earth,
And man perceives her mystic spell.

A tender grass the background makes
For the tiny, wispy flower,
And we wonder that they dare to brave
Winter's cold, forbidding bower.

Easily crushed by vagrant feet
They come to secret life,
And we find them in the morning dew,
Shyly smiling with spirits blithe.

Their tender freshness gladdens one
Who knows that fairy spring
Will once again rule all the land
And back to earth her sweetness bring.

SYMPHONY   Cyvia Russian

A symphony to me is this:
Love and tears and joy and bliss.

A symphony to me is more:
Waves against a barren shore.

A lovely strain brings warmth and cheer
To every wish that's found sincere.

It takes from hearts of those who dream
A melody for its new theme.

BLOODSHED   Glen Schaefer

Here lives BLOODSHED
Here at home
There on the battlefield
It lives in many ways.
Through fighting, disaster and accident
It is nursed by carelessness
Fed by war, and brought on by violence
Welcomed by warmongers
Dreaded by families
And abolished by peace
Yes, here lives BLOODSHED

THE SEA   James Lott

As I look out o'er the sea from my place
                here on the shore,
I behold on it a beauty never marvelled
                at before.
The rhythmed undulations of the waves
                upon the sand;
The mighty dashing of the billows against
                the rocks in manner grand.

Joining us with other peoples, the sea
                resting in its bed;
Separating always the great lands on which
                we tread.
And, as the wind comes gently blowing,
                as the wind that follows rain,
The sharp sea air thrills my body with
                a feeling I cannot quite explain.

AMERICA   George Fredrickson

Brawny grim-faced workman,
Rolling up his shirt sleeves,
Flexing his sinewy, powerful
                muscles,
Lifting his tools once again to
        regain and rebuild a shattered
        world.

INSINCERITY   Ilona R. Bein

How awful it is, saying something that is false,
    that comes not from the heart,
But from the surface of cold lips with no meaning
    from the start.

This thing called insincerity numbing one's thoughts
    and feelings as well,
Is something which insidiously finds deceitful tales
    to tell.

And all the while having deceivingly pretended,
Like an actor who cunningly plays his role until
    his part has ended,

So it continues with a new person and a fresh start
    for its own selfish cause;
Thus the actor plays on, encouraged by resounding
    self-applause.

THE CROCUS   Carol Wheeler

I saw her standing in the shade
    Beneath a willow tree,
A herald of the coming spring
    Which seemed to beckon me.
With eyes glued to her beauty
    I found she was so fair
That I could hardly keep my breath
    When I first saw her there.
I often had seen others,
    But they were dull and drab
Compared to this rare beauty,
    Such slender grace she had
Alone she stood, yet lonely not,
    For dignity had she.
It seemed that God's hand placed her there
    Beneath that willow tree.

MOTHER'S HANDS   Ann Di Maio

Mother's hands are not long, slender, and snowy white
Like a model's on a hand cream ad.
They are short and thick, with a gold wedding band encircling them.
Often her hands are rough, and her nails, jagged
From the toils around the house.
But when she cared for me when I was a child,
Her hands weren't rough and jagged,
Instead, they were to me like velvety petals
Of a beautiful white rose.
Her hands have come from God,
And though they aren't beautiful to others,
To God and me, they are her perfect attribute.

ECHOES . Barbara-Ann Bonner

A hound-dog howls.
A long, low wail.
A note
Held for an eternity,
Reaching to the harvest moon,
And echoing back again
To bound and re-bound
Between husks of corn
Standing
In an open field.

MOUNTAIN MAGIC   Rex S. Burns

The deep purple shadows slowly thicken,
The bullfrog's song begins to quicken,
Campfire smoke hangs low in the valley,
And the quail begins his nightly rally.
Softly comes the call of an owl;
The contented chirping of other fowl.
Stars like violets shyly peep
Through the ragged clouds and twilight deep.
Towering mountains hem all sides,
And hoary oaks in the valley reside.
Deer float quietly to the stream
Only to freeze at the cougar's scream.
Twilight heals the day's tragic
Happenings with its mountain magic.

SUNSET   Beth Ann Rausch

God picks up His palette
And swishes great streaks of rose
Across the darkening sky.
Encasing the horizon in a purple flame
Bathing the world in an ethereal light
As He strives to show us the wonders of day
Before He pulls down the curtain of night.

MY STAR   Jimmy Trentham

'Tis but a streak of light in a
              dimension of time,
'Tis but a few grains of dust as it
              drops softly to the earth,
But yesterday, yes, yesterday, it was
              a glowing star, so brave, so beautiful
        in the heavens where God had placed it.
But yesternight as I gazed upon the gardens
              of heavens,
I saw this star so young, so bright.
Then suddenly a flash, a beam of light
              was seen in the sky.
My star was gone and in its place
There appeared only space, a darken space
Then at my feet there dropped a stone,
              only a few grains of dust.

THAT MYSTERIOUS LIQUID   Marilyn Loughary

Water is such a funny thing,
It can laugh, and talk, and cry.
It can be a rushing mountain stream,
Or in silent stillness lie.

It can be a bubbling brook,
Or a rising crest of rain,
A slowly creeping glacier rug,
Or a wide, deep river lane.

Water is a treacherous flood,
Or perhaps a starlit pool
That has been filled by God's own tears
Of raindrops, clear and cool.

DRIFTING   Charlotte Hofer

Space . . . . ,
That infinite heaven of blue
With sun and moon and stars
And us . . . . , drifting.
Unbelievable in measure of miles . . . . so endless.
Never to be understood by mind of man
How . . . . all this came about
Why . . . . was anything ever?
God . . . . alone
Can solve this riddle . . .
He holds the key . . . so wondrous . . . awesome.
The answer . . . is in Heaven.

SONNET   Andrew Torchia

Should not one try to take the yellow grain,
The hot black oil, the forest green, and use
Them for a better land, a gentler plain
Where one may sing and laugh, where one may choose
Freedom from self-fear, distrust, and the rest
That now can only foul our once fair sky?
It is a large thing to do; it is at best
Only a blind beginning, but one may try.
And when the task is done, what then, my friend;
Have we finished what we set out to do?
To ignorance, distrust, put we an end
To them all? No, friend, the job is not through,
For having moved the grain, the soil, the sod,
One must move Man, the other work of God.

THE MOUSE   Janice Nelson

All dressed in gray a little mouse
    Has made his home within my house,
And every night and every dawn
    I say, "I wish that mouse were gone."
But what a quiet soul is he,
    As anyone can plainly see.
My house is large, my hearth is wide,
    There's room for him and me beside
Ah, yes, when the lights go out
    He likes to slyly creep about.
And help himself to what he sees
    Without once saying, "If you please."

PARTIAL PLAINT   Peggy Garner

I sing, and the Muse's ears are deaf;
I sing, and the little, dried-up leaf
Waves on in the grim, gray drip of rain;
I sing, and there's none the less of pain
Nor any the more of golden light in any part
Of anything, save in my own heart.

INSPIRATION   Margaret Tremain

He sits alone .... still .... quiet .... deep in
                              thought.
His hands lie motionless upon the keys.
Then, suddenly, he smiles and lifts his head,
And music pours forth from his inspired hands.
His fingers ripple over the keys as
A stream flows endlessly along its banks.
He plays .... and birds raise forth their
                    glorious songs;
The pine trees rustle in the falling rain;
The wind blows o'er the meadows still
And yet grows stronger till it swells in fury ....
And dies again, to leave the earth in quiet.
He stops .... and takes his hands from the keys.
Again they lie so quiet in his lap.
He sits alone, still .... quiet .... deep in thought,
'Till inspiration .... gone .... comes once
          again.

THE PEACEMAKER   Mary Ann Puwalowski

Oh, the burden was heavy;
The time was long --
When deep despair
Captured me there.

O, life was futile;
What purpose had I here?
Leave me, pain of despair and
Come, oh joy of yester-year.

But wait -- A sudden, fleeting glance
Upon Sister's face did fall;
Oh, the glory of it, the reassurance
                    and the peace!
For Sister smiled --
.... That was all.

HOME   Kathryn Cozad

A home is where a heart can stay
When hands and feet are far away.
A home is where a child can play.

A home is where the life so bright
Reminds the traveler in the night
That somewhere there is rest and light.

A home is where old age, content,
Remembers what a life has meant.

SEA MAGIC   Anne Adams

Waves sweep up on the desolate shore,
Whisper the moaning music of sea;
Foam curls and writhes on the hard sand-floor
Stirring among its own debris.

Froth pulls back, down the sloping beach,
Meets another billow that breaks with a roar,
The tumbled surges coil each over each
Slide back to the throat of the sea once more.

Through swirling of fog drifting sea is heard
As a far away boom on an unseen strand,
Till wind blowing through lifts the veil and brings
Sea-scents to disenchanted land.

ETERNAL TOMB   Clay Cribbs

I hear the sea, I hear the sea,
The breakers roar and call to me.
My father's blood was mixed with brine,
And as his son, so shall be mine.

Hark, listen, the waves still call,
They know they shall be my fall.
It is the sea and not the earth,
That shall entomb me, after birth.

Low beneath the waves shall I lie,
Rock and watch all time go by.
And then my soul shall never bleed,
For the waves' call I did heed.

SIMILE   Esther Romero

My life is like a calendar
Alike and new all year,
Each time I go to see it
A page has disappeared,
A page that in my memory
Brings forth a smile or tear.

CREATION'S MASTERPIECE   Lorraine Clarke

You are beautiful.
Your robes, woven of the sky and sea;
Your form, so slender, silent, strong;
Lovely hands and quiet eyes;
And in those eyes
Mirrored every cup of sorrow that you had.

You are beautiful,
With a soft ethereal beauty that rises
With the perfume of your soul,
And from the canvas of human misconception unfetters -
A dove, soaring from the moor.

You are beautiful.
I have painted you thus;
Yet I know your beauty comes not by my hand,
But by the hand of God within you.

Like Adonis of old,
I live but half my life upon this earth.
The other part I wander all alone inside myself -
In search of peace.

You are peace.
I cast myself at your feet.
Gather me that I may sleep, serene.

LA INTRUSA   Roberta Howard

She stooped to warm her hands before the fire;
Pale hands they were, and thin, and purple cold.
The group around the hearthblaze turned in ire;
One let her pass, and passing, she made bold
To crouch e'en lower toward the friendly flames
And then, when she was toasted to the bone,
The close-knit circle closed before her eyes
And left her - hurt, numb, groping, and alone.

TINKLING KEYS   Gail Price

The tinkling of keys in a faraway room
Reminds me somewhat of a lily in bloom.
Fleeing arpeggios soaring so high,
It seems they go up to the sky,
And heavy chords with their grotesque impressions
Fill my heart with fear and obsessions.
If you doubt my observations,
  Then use your imaginations.

TO THE FLAG   Bob Oldenburg

Oh, lady of democracy
Emblem of God's supremacy;
Thou art a gleaming beacon fair
That guides men from destruction's lair.

Thy skirt is striped with streaks of gore
That was shed by men thy preservation for.
A dome of blue o'er thy head is hung,
While a crown of stars all thy glory sung.

Since democracy's dawn thy banner has waved
And always will while liberty is saved.
Oh, may God, our Father, with mercy look down,
And keep thy bright glory till the trumpet does sound.

NO SCHOOL TODAY   Edward May

I'm feeling indisposed today
In this new and brilliant dawn.
When school calls I will not heed
I greet it with a languid yawn.

Oh, not too sick for lunch or sup
My conscience won't let me sleep.
But much too sick for getting up
So for today school will keep.

I'll find little time to read
Let those who can, keep the pace.
Of school I shall pay no heed
Today I'll skip the human race.

THE CLOUDS   Patricia Gertmann

The clouds seem like pieces of beautiful cloth,
All of different textures and hues.
Some are like lovely dimity,
And seem to float and fold in the breeze,
Some are like sheer marquisette,
That curtains the windows of the sky.
And some like smooth linen,
Covering the soft fleece
That serves as angel pillows.

ON PATTERN   Marilyn Mansfield

Brown graceful fingers, as the swallows fly,
Dart in and out among the homely strands.
And as the end of patient toil draws nigh
A pattern is the joy of weavers' hands.
Or ugly caterpillars strip the leaves
And wrap themselves in grave-clothes cold and white
'Til spring when all the world no more deceives
And butterflies dance gaily in the light.

We praise the pattern - shun the simple thread;
Condemn the caterpillar's lowly birth.
The old man merits praise when he is dead
But still we doubt the young man's promised worth.
For they believe who see the rose, indeed,
But God believed the promise of the seed.

SERENITY   Ardell Spang

The mountains 'round me in grandeur sweep.
The climb to the top is very steep,
But there the eye for miles can see
The boundless range of vale and lea.
The long, hard journey is repaid
By seeing just what nature's made.

The last rays of the dying sun
Foretell that the day is nearly done.
And into the valleys far below
The velvety shadows softly go.
The wispy clouds the sun refines
And each one elegantly lines.
The troubles of the day are past,
And peacefulness is found at last.

GIFT TO LIFE   Marlene Dorland

Life is a dying ember,
  without fuel to maintain its glow.

He, who lives, must replenish life
  with more than bare necessity.

Four fuels: toil, felicity, sorrow, and rest
  enliven the ember
To a rushing, maddening life-blood stream.

TO RIDICULE   Marlene Idso

Folks laugh at my auto;
Make fun of my shack;
They even must sneer
At the clothes on my back!

Folks laugh at my livestock
And scoff at my farming;
They never stop jeering,
It's terribly alarming!

I can easily take it;
But then ... what is worse
They'll turn right around and
R i d i c u l e my verse!

INSPIRATION   Roger Cook

Inspiration! What a fight --
   Inspiration in the night.
Thoughts come and thoughts go,
   But will inspiration come? No!

Eyes weary and red-rimmed ---
   Noises gone and lights dimmed.
Oh inspiration, come to me as a million
   thoughts I mull,
In the awesome silence of the long
   night's lull.

So, students all, list to me ---
   If from worry, you can remain free.
Remember, it's a most unpleasant sensation --
   To search in vain for inspiration.

PASSE   Anna Koo

The stage is still, the lights are dimmed, and here
Am I alone, applause still haunting me
Where'ere I go. To see this once again,
My mind recalls the time when I was star
And cheers were meant for me. Success was mine
To have, to keep, but now, young stars have reached
And passed my golden years. Within their hearts,
Within their blood, the stage forever more
Will dwell, until perhaps, as I, they'll leave
Obsessed by ghosts of years gone by.
The years elapsed and here am I once more,
Brought back by love of stage within my soul.
Success again will ne'er be mine, but here
I shall remain, content, although pass'e.

WISH   Ruth Coffman

Give me not the million singing birds of dawn,
their polyglot of notes assails my ears,
Nor acre upon acre of burnished Autumn trees,
each burning brighter than the next.
Rather would I have a lone robin's song,
coloring the silent, dying day,
Or one flower from Paradise.

MY BROTHER   Richard Dyson

My brother is a gifted man
With coffers full of gold.
My brother is a ragged man
Whose pockets nothing hold.
My brother is a savage
As wild as the sea is blue.
My brother is not only he
But you and you and you!

My brother is a rich man
With barrels of priceless oil.
My brother is a common thief
Who takes while others toil.
My brother is a lonely man
Whose God he never knew.
My brother is not only he
But you and you and you!

ILLUSION   Elizabeth Crosby

The dancers were swaying in diaphanous mist
With a tilt, and a turn; a graceful breeze
Caressing each feather-light Terpsichore,
As they flew over hills and high trees;
Dipping and gliding on silvery toes
They sent their skirts billowing as they danced,
Then I discovered not dancers at all
But soft white clouds which held me entranced.

PLEA FOR PEACE   Constance Rosner

As tension for my fate grips me with fear
And dreams seem shrouded, I attempt to grope
For threads of ambition, now a thin hope
In this smothering fog that does not clear.
There was the other war five years ago,
But I was too young then to know turmoil
That laid the men beneath the seas and soil
For peace on earth that was e'er to be so.

I know well I must not give way to fear
But we, the helpless children of the last,
Are in a war shadow that has been cast
By men not heeding the peace pleas they hear
From youths like me, who desperately ask,
"For peace, must earth be void of man and beast?"

EVALUATION   Carolyn Peeples

We constantly evaluate
    the services of men,
The contributions, large and small,
    of strangers and of kin.

But often we imperfectly
    bestow our praise awry,
Influenced by the gold and splendor
    that easily catch our eye.

This, though, does not change truth itself,
    nor honest efforts made
That in all right deserve reward
    for common service paid.

SHADOWS   Barbara Bell

Shadows leaning on the ground
Are velvet patches dancing 'round.
Bowing with the zephyr's sway,
The shadows linger low to play.
Waltzing with the winsome breeze,
They dive and wander through the trees.

Connie Klaaren

Who builds the world, the patterns weave
Of peace and war which gladden and grieve
The thoughts of men who live and die
In respect of ideals, high
In men who loved their land.

In suffering 'tis He that does relieve
The pains of what they should achieve,
He is the one who lends the joys or can deny,
Who builds the world.

Who else from the earth will leave
The gift He knew that He'd receive?
'Tis He who brings life where bodies lie,
And puts the sun up in the sky,
Who builds the world.

THE UNDYING LOVE OF GOD
Katherine Orban

Amid the toil and the strife,
A part of everyone's daily life,
Comes the very sweet pleasure
Of sharing such a priceless treasure,
      The undying love of God.

When one's soul grows tired and weary,
On a day seemingly useless and dreary,
Driving all cares forever out of sight,
Comes a ray of hope and light
      The undying love of God.

When stilled waters are greatly troubled,
And light burdens are suddenly doubled,
An up-turned face to the star-studded blue
Will bring peace and joy to the faithful few,
      From the undying love of God.

ARTIST'S REVERIE   Margaret Faust

I wish I were an artist, with bright paint and brush in hand,
Alone with my imagination and lots of Time to spend.
Whenever I'd feel blue, I'd paint a rainbow in the sky;
And spindly pines reflected in a crystal lake near by.
In winter weather cold and dreary,
I'd paint some roses red and cheery.
I'd paint the lilacs lavender soaked with early morning dew.
On my canvas I'd recapture the twilight's purple hue
And the fiery sunset before it slips beyond the blue.

UNCONQUERABLE ENEMY   Bruce Simnacher

Through the ages, man has battled me.
We have fought upon both land and sea,
Yet never have I halted my preying upon man.
I have annihilated both family and clan.
No man escapes my watchful eye.
At my name, brave men flee, women and children cry.
I am man's unconquerable foe,
For no man can live where I cannot go.
I am always greeted with great sorrow
By men whom I shall meet tomorrow.
All mankind fears my icy breath.
Man's eternal enemy, I am death.

FAITH   Joyce Waller

As I was sitting by my window pane,
I watched the snowflakes softly fall to earth;
On house, on tree, they found a second birth,
Those downy fragments of celestial claim
Whose transcendental laws do not proclaim,
But lo! the lurid sun came out with mirth,
So soon the transient flakes were in a dearth,
And once again the landscape was the same.

Oh give us faith in Thee and man, I pray;
The seasons come and go unquestioned still,
The rainbow, after winds have rant and raved,
The quiet dusk that ends a perfect day;
Enhance our hearts with tranquil thoughts until
We feel serene and know that we are saved.

LIFE   Lois Whitmayer

My life is but a brief spark
From the flame of time,
An ember from the hearth of the ages,
A mere pinpoint of light escaped
From the brilliance of eternity.
Yet to me, my small spark
Is more infinitely precious
Than the flame of time,
Or the fires of history.

WAR   Charles Chavarria

What black and wicked creature art thou, War,
With outstretched arms that grasp for harmless prey,
Not satisfied, but always seizing more,
To fill thy greedy stomach day by day?
What devastating demon can thou be,
Who strips the earth of able bodied youth
And throws them into death's infernal sea,
Or leaves their bodies mangled so uncouth?
And yet despite the terror you do spread,
There will be those will still remain your friend,
And lure you on to other prey instead.
They care not for the ones that they offend
For they use you, O War, as but a slave,
To get possessive power which they so crave.

REMEMBER   Vincent Cekela, Jr.

Remember the day of Pearl Harbor?
Remember the time of peace?
Remember that day in August,
When "all" war did cease?

Remember the years that followed,
The coming of the end?
Remember the months of gladness,
Which we did gayly spend?

Remember now the conflict great,
Which Red Koreans made?
But don't forget the price
Which we have dearly paid.

THE BOOK OF LIFE   Rita Gallagher

What beauty lies between its dull, drab covers?
Come, pick it up, else how are you to know
Of the story inscribed there on its pages,
Of the words marching stiffly row on row
Across a pure white desert.

What fable will it speak to entertain us?
What real truth to make us understand
That we are nothing but for God's great mercy,
That He is leading us by the hand
Across a stormy desert.

And when we reach the end of the last chapter
And the book of life is closed for the world to see
He will come with His Mother and my Father
And He'll raise His voice and say aloud to me,
"Come, to my flowering desert."

REVELATION   Mary McCall

I travel o'er mountains, o'er burning sand,
O'er rocky waste by wind unfanned,
'Neath towering trees, past rivers deep,
Through valleys of eternal sleep.

I look at raging ocean surf,
Or walk along the shadowed turf
Of forests green, and have in me
A feeling of Divinity.

NIGHT THOUGHTS   Jane Ellen Toates

When day has forced its final streaked glare
And died away - and darkness has erased
All color from the boughs, of leaves now bare,
Their twisted silhouettes in black are traced
Upon the crescent moon. And mist surrounds
Each corporal thing, as though in stygian gloom
Grim Charon should grant passage past the bounds
Of River Styx and out of sleep's dark tomb.
How long shall this Eternity remain?
Is this the threatened doom of all mankind?
Shall we Aurora's light again regain,
Or has the light of day been left behind?
But when this transient death again has passed,
Another dawn will bloom again at last.

THE MIST   Paul Casey

The mist was drifting slowly along
   The forest path and glade;
It wept upon the leafy fern
   And over log decayed
It passed a tiny fawn asleep,
   And made the shadows fade.
It wandered through, along with me,
Those things that God had made!

TIME   Darlene Lusmann

Upon a hill of endless time I stand
Looking across the sea of ages past,
What is to come is in God's loving hand;
Shadow of life will but a moment last.

The wise mountains against the cloudless sky
Tell of the miracles of glories gone,
But far ahead from cavernous depth's cry
We hear but cannot see the future's dawn.

We ask what time is and was and shall be,
No answers our questions and our fears;
We count our years which like the wind do flee,
No one but God can wipe away our tears.

MUSIC   Ruth Hodges

Sweet music seems to fill the air,
With chords both soft and low,
It seems like echoes from a bell,
Or pale light in after-glow.

The rich chords tremble on each star,
That twinkles up on high,
They glide and float like purple clouds,
That grace the twilight sky.

What is this music clear and sweet,
That comes from nature's heart?
It is man's joyful praise to God,
For gifts He doth impart.

THE END OF TODAY   Thomas Lee Reeves

'Twill not be long, what I have to say,
For I, as others, see dusk not far away.
    Yes, time is fleeting; day will soon be past,
Use well these last few minutes - the sky is over-cast.
    Hurry! Hurry! A little time remains!
Cease at once to loiter; strain the boilers,
                    the spinning frames.
    Build new roads, lay new track,
Time is almost gone - the sky is black.
    With finishing touch inspect each task,
Lock each door, such little light lasts.
    Now stop each engine, refuel each one,
Set the clocks for tomorrow - today is done.

JANUARY THAW   Camilla Lorenc

The air is soft and sweet
With January thaw
That dampens your feet, but
Braces your soul.
Just another prank of
Spring, teasing, luring
Us to believe that she is here
And then throws another fistfull
Of snow into your face.
The air is bitter again, with
Intense cold, but somewhere, Oh,
Somewhere, I hear a voice telling me
That it can't last forever.

SPRINGTIME   Inge Klein

Green valleys sparkle new.
Wild flowers drip with dew.
New sun, new dress, new birth,
Embrace the whole wide earth.
It's spring, the birds all sing;
Come join our happy ring.

The earth all dressed in green,
Her fragrance pungent, keen,
Blesses each new budding flower,
Kisses each cloud-tipped tower;
Rejoices that spring is here
With pleasant voices near.

MY PIECE OF GOLD   Helen Montgomery

This piece of gold is mine to spend,
Upon myself or upon some friend.
This one choice is mine to make,
With much more than a coin at stake.
For this gold, which I will spend
Is my life from beginning to end.
Precious life, if rightly spent
Upon my friend my attention bent.

SUNSET   Joyce Zehr

Each eve I climb my hill
And survey my kingdom, quiet and still,
There I sit, by the world forgot,
To watch the Master Painter and His plot.

Each stroke will change the scene --
From a velvet purple to a bluish gleam;
With all the pinks and golds there,
The Northern Lights cannot compare.

As its glorious rays streak the sky,
The Sun will say a fond good-bye.
Night's entrancing cloak will soon
Hide all lights, save the silvery stars and moon.

THE CITYSIDE   Elsie Heyler

You hear about the countryside
It's sweet, clean and wholesome.
Who likes the noisy cityside?
It's dirty, mean and loathsome.

The city's 'scrapers brush the sky
While farm and country hug the ground.
At night the city breathes and sighs
And her brick arms, us, surround.

You've spirit for countryside and farm
But we city folks have our own.
It's just as earnest and just as warm,
Spirit of our city: spirit of home.

ATOM BOMB   Bobby Perry

Servant, yet master; friend and yet foe;
    Builder of a wonderful tomorrow,
And yet destroyer of all that we know;
    Creator of happiness or sorrow,
What fate or future do you plan for men?

We dreamed you, designed you, and built you;
    Your ponderous power is the work of our hands.
Our benefits from your might have thus far been few;
    You have maimed our people, devastated our lands.
Will our future with you be better or worse?

HIDDEN ECSTASY   Jane Vogele

Unlatch the door of the mind of dreams
And through it, first in mystic fog,
Then transformed into a seemingly tangible existence
Seep one's ideal desires and unexpressed wishes.
The dancing images of a radiant fire, or perhaps,
Some untamed wind playing on the bared branches of
                        a graceful tree,
May incite the mind, and slowly,
Without one's voluntary consent,
Lower a dim, undefined shadow over a conscious mind.
When having dismissed all earthly cares
Does one sense the flavor of this imaginary world,
And pause, and dream.

NIGHT THOUGHTS OF A SOLDIER IN KOREA
                        Gaye Streid

Tomorrow and tomorrow and tomorrow -
What will that day reveal, as the sun
Finally will rise from its heavenly bed?
Will it be like today and yesterday
And all the days before? Out, out to
The battlefields, where many of my buddies
Lie, in peaceful sleep. No more to fight
For things they love or love the things
For which they fought. I hear the sound
And fury of some distant cannon roar.
I know it's time to go. Oh, God, please,
Give me the strength, courage,
And faith, to face another tomorrow.

LAUGHTER   Anne Heininger

Laughter comes
from a spring in the heart.

It bubbles up
with gurgling happiness
to quench the thirst
of the world for joy

PERPETUAL NIGHT   Robert J. Obert

What would I do if darkness should descend?
Flee mortal hearths, like mole, Aurora's light;
And bear alone the never-ending Night;
Or must my care on others' watch depend?
Yet futile as these selfish courses wend,
May Sorrow never reach that awful height,
With Reason hurled aloft by Nature's slight,
That I, an anguished curse to God would send.

In time a greater Light would filter through,
Unveiling His ambrosial gift to Man,
A glimpse of Nature's wonders brought to view
By Ear, and Touch, and Mind - Blindness' Gulf they span;
My blessings, ever old and yet anew,
In retrospect, Life's diverse Caravan.

ALONE   Nanci Levine

My love, my love, return to me once more;
Return before the glowing embers fade
To gray, and bite into my heart's own core.
You leave me sad, and cold, and lost, afraid

To face the world. This surely must I do
When yet within I shrink from the ordeal.
I tell myself that I must wait for you
To make me proud when you your love reveal.

What reason I, to laugh, to sing, to sigh,
To ask for joy or happiness, today,
When I, bedecked with sorrow's binding tie,
Pray God to send you back along my way?

Am I to walk this lonely, dreary road,
From this day on to live in sad abode?

ANOTHER DAY   Billy Heflin

The sun came up behind the hills,
And the shadows of the night crept away.
There to us was born a day of thrills;
At least another day.
　　Another day of fighting;
　　Another day of hunger;
　　Another day of killing;
　　Another night of wonder;
And then another day.

CANDLE   Edward M. Zimmermann

The candle burns,
With a flame for its light;
Its heat shows the world,
As a lifelong fight.
The tallow is the symbol
Of the struggle and the fears;
For it shows fierce reality,
As it sheds man's tears.
And then the hard, solid candle,
From where the tallow came
Soon will be gone,
At the passing of a name.

SPRING MAGIC   Sharon Jean
                           Merkel

A strange and unknown world it seemed
　　When I awoke today;
Instead of "purple mountain majesties"
　　I saw the hills were gray.

The soft green carpet on my lawn
　　Had turned to ermine white,
And saucy robins wondered why
　　They'd made their northward flight.

But peeping from its hood of snow
　　Bright crocus smiled and said,
"This storm was just in time, you know,
　　To bring the tulips red."

So strange and unknown, though it seems,
　　The world is wondrous bright;
When snow and March make up a team
　　They bring Spring in overnight.

SAND DUNES   Don Myers

The dunes of sand forever shift -
They know not where they go;
They cover tales of days gone by,
And hide from man the signs of foe.

The drifting sands shelter ruins of ancient times -
Yet in their endless motion cover works of present days;
And in this eternal change uncover ancient culture's signs,
And leave for men in years to come a history of our mankind.

THIS WORLD OF OURS   Colleen Brulatte

Wouldn't this whole world be nice
    If it "suffered" a total lack of vice;
If we had no need to fear
    Our destruction ever near;
If we could be always happy and gay
    Like little children on Christmas day;
If we had no fear of Stalin's errors,
    Covering the world with vice and terror;
If we could live through a peaceful daybreak
    Without the fear of an atom bomb quake?
What a pleasant world this would be
    For all concerned .... you and me.

SHEPHERD'S FALLS (Wind River, Washington)
                          Dave Narver

The falls of grandeur lie in sunshine bright
Just as the time when redmen speared steelhead.
In summer days, the deer still browse and bed
In shelter given by the gorge, and light
Still glistens from yon rock, where squaws all night
Did clean the kill. The river now does wed
The sky and water, toward one rainbow led,
And fish still jump the falls in all their might.

The trees may live or die on your great banks,
Oh falls of stately splendor, but you flow
Unceasingly. Wild animals do want
Your shadowed gorge. They pause to give their
                                        thanks
And leave. But you persistent downward go,
And all the decades past and present haunt.

END OF A STORM   Edward Steele

The foaming smashing of the wintry sea,
Upon the jagged rocks on the lee,
Makes tunes in rhyme with the wild lashings of wind
That scream to God in outrageous din.
While in the darkened sky o'er head
Storm the hard pressed thunderhead,
But a brilliant ray approaches from the East
Bringing with it a promise of peace.

KING ARTHUR   Sue Graves

A king there was and Arthur was his name,
Throughout the land there spreads this tale of fame:
How from the rank of squire to king he rose,
And how he overcame his country's foes.
Excalibur, his magic sword of old,
For ancient Britain won her rights untold,
His knights for chivalry were ne'er surpassed,
For courtliness to them was not a mask.
When death became his final foe to face,
He ne'er despaired but met it with a grace.
When England looks upon a troubled shore,
Arthur is there - so goes the ancient lore.

THE SUBWAY AT NIGHT   Jack Landau

                Local
Slowly, to a noisy stop
The doors open wide;
The people pour as ants
To a narrow dimlit platform,
Like a pitiful blind beggar
Asking, "Pencils, pencils, pencils,"
Then moving aimlessly
          Into definite oblivion.

              Express
So efficient, so fast,
Looking scornfully back
As it juggernauts past
Minor stations in the darkness;
From a black blanket
Emerging swiftly into
Pale cement and tile,
Then moving quickly on,
          Into definite oblivion.

BLUEBELLS   Miyuki Kagawa

When morning's curtain rises
To a symphony of winds,
And the sun throws his glittering spotlight
Upon the stage of spring,
Bluebells
In azure petal gowns
Dance gaily out
On little pollen feet.

SPRING FEVER   Zelda Davis

The pale blue sky
    Is whipped with cream
And in each eye
    Visions of a dream
Long with a sigh
    To stroll down the lane.

The sun is high
    O'er the sparkling stream
No time to cry.
    Swing on a sunbeam
Like fields of rye
    Free as summer rain.

IMPRESSIONS AT A FOOTBALL GAME
                        Ann Brunskill
Gay clothes,
Assorted styles;
Flushed faces,
Sparkling smiles;
    Brilliant red and white.

Whirling girls,
Dancing pom poms;
Leaping legs,
Beating tom toms;
    Rhythmic red and white.

Graceful passes,
Swirling hips;
Flashing helmets,
Bleeding lips;
    Stalwart red and white.

DREAMER   Halton Charlton

Oh, every man dreams of just this one thing -
What joy and wealth that it could bring.
No one's dreams will be the same at all -
And my dream, in the lower rank, shouldn't fall.

I often see that beautiful one -
With others, having blissful fun.
Yes, I dream of loving her true -
On yonder crest, just below the blue.

My wealth, the moneyed rich, would not surpass -
If I could love and cherish this one lass.
But if our love never be, before I pass earth's door -
God grant, she be beautiful, as now, forevermore.

TEA   John Cavanagh

Ladies sit and sip gossip,
Delighting in the cream of scandal;
They sugar it with falsehood,
Exaggeration is a delicious biscuit.
They talk much, say little,
And all one hears is the clink,
Clink, clink, clink,
Of their teacup mouths.
Have they nothing better to do?

A MASTERPIECE OF ROSE MADDER
Barbara James

Cold canvas, you mock the very warmth
            of burnt umber eyes,
You seem to defy the pigments to conquer
            your barren surface.
Perhaps rose madder would disguise you.

If I but put the right stroke here and there,
            you will win a moral victory.
Condemned canvas! I have a smiling shadow
            and you have won temporarily.
Perhaps rose madder would disguise you.

Now I have finished - the warm burnt umber
            eyes reflect icy stares
Oh! The smiling shadows are contorted
            lines of scorn.
Perhaps rose madder would disguise you.

WIND AND SAND   Royce Dyer

The day was dawning clear and bright and warm
Without a sign of wind to blow the trees;
But with the rising of the sun there came a breeze
Which grew in force to be a howling storm.
The morning sky grew dark with flying sand;
Along the streets were blowing dust and trash;
The sweeping wind caused limbs of trees to clash
And piled great drifts of sand upon good land.

The sun at noon rose high into the sky;
The raging wind died low; then ceased to blow.
The air became clean as afternoon grew nigh,
For wind and sand had finished one day's show.
At dusk a pleasant breeze began to sigh,
While bathed in clouds of pink the sun sank low.

THE SEASONS OF THE YEAR   Anne Brown

The spring had watched us come
Together here.
The summer eyed us laughing,
Very near.
While we were walking slowly
Toward the bend,
Came fall; the winter saw us
To the end.

CAN STILL BE SPRING   J. Ann Wyer

Fleecy white clouds floating
Calmly across the lustrous pale-blue sky;
Soft, sweet melodies sung by a chorus
Of multi-colored birds;
The tiny head of the green crocus popping
Himself above the dark-brown earth,
These things are the beginning of spring.

Spring is not only a time of year,
But a feeling in the hearts of the creatures
Of the world.
It awakens life anew to all of us.

Even when the dull, dark days of coldest winter
Are hovering over us,
In our hearts can still be spring.

THE FIRST SNOW   Beverly Thalman

The wind blows through the leafless trees
    The sky - a leaden gray
And shivering in the winter breeze
    The people hurry on their way
Long since the birds in headlong flight
    Have left for sunnier clime
Their old time haunts beside the brook
    Are hung with frost and rime
But laughing children leap about
    As they run in childish glee
In happy anticipation shout
    The first winter snowflakes to see.

LOVE AND INSPIRATION   Muriel Wood

Love is a mater of inspiration
    I can not for one moment doubt it.
Poets need to have love within them;
    Their writings are worthless without it.
One must have loved to be able to hate,
    Those emotions are not far apart,
One cannot fix a staid line between them;
    Do they both not connect to the heart?
One must have felt love to experience sorrow;
    One must have had friends to now feel alone;
For who can take from us those few little pleasures
    Which we in our lives have not ever known?
And love alone speaks with fluent pen,
    For verse is written from hearts of men.

TRAILS   Linda Blackaby

The old trails,
The dusty trails,
Where the covered wagons rolled
Through winter's snow and summer's sun
To the West in search of gold.

The high trails,
The sky trails,
Where the rocket planes go by
It's our land,
A free land,
Where the mountains reach the sky.

I WOULD NOT   Margaret Sluder

I would not want pride as high as the mountains,
Nor sin as deep as the sea;
The humbleness of the valleys appeals more to me.

I would not want a heart as cold as snow,
Nor a spirit like a storm;
The kindness of the heavens appeals more to me.

I would not want a voice like lightning,
Nor to be as selfish as the wind;
The loveliness of the clouds appeals more to me.

SING TO ME   Rosemary Butler

Sing to me, you hills of beauty
Sing to me of azure sky
Sing to me of unknown beauty
Overlooked by human eye.
Sing to me the tale of woodlands
Of the quiet, peaceful life
Sing to me your lifetime story
Of the struggle, and the strife.

TEMPUS FUGIT   Leslie Green

Counting your life away
The clocks on the wall, in the hall,
The ones that are small,
The ones that are tall,
Are stealing your life, through night, during day,
        Away, far away.

Hearing each tick,
List to the sounds of death's measured pounds;
They're beating in rhyme
Taking your life, through night, during day,
        Away, far away.

With each moment parting,
The clocks madly beating, the seconds so fleeting,
Death with its greeting,
The grave you'll be meeting,
Are saying to you, through night, during day,
        "Away, far away."

LONELINESS   Barbara Craven

Loneliness breathes,
And her breathing falls, like mist,
Around my head.

Loneliness sighs softly
Like the mournfulness
Of rustling air through the catacombs;
Bitter is her cry, like the sound of wind in dead trees.

Just as the mighty ocean waves
Charge boldly on toward adventure,
Only to fade into dying riplets
That meet dead sand,
So I come face to face with loneliness.

Loneliness breathes,
And her breathing falls, like mist,
Around my head.

CHALLENGE TO THE RAIN   Wilkes Berry

O Rain! Why sendeth not thy torrent?
Why sendeth not thy flood?
O Mighty Despot! Why send a whispering idiot,
The mist around my door?
Why cometh not thyself, great lord,
That rules the dark-skied day?
We know thy power and thy might.
Why showeth not thy face?
We would meet thee and defeat thee,
Raging fool with only voice and threats.

THE DAWN OF PEACE   Carol Frederick

Is there peace in the world?
Is there love secure?
Is there any council beyond this sea of sin?
Yes, salvation, strong and mighty!
Where all is well with God;
Where Christ will dwell within --
There is a Dawn of Peace,
Where fiery tongues will cease;
There is a place of quiet rest
From all the human, lusty zest;
There is a dawn for everyone,
If they will turn to God and Son.

IMMACULATE CONCEPTION   Mary Ann Donovan

Angels stoop in wond'ring awe,
Their trembling hearts enraptur'd, bend
Low,
My heart,
In perfect stillness,
Thrills before the radiance,
Worships in the glory,
Of the love-borne realization -
Immaculate!

A PRAYER FOR PEACE   John Davis

O God, whose natural beauty's loved
By most who look upon this world --
This world of wond'rous trees and
                    flow'rs,
Streams and mountains,
Rain and snow --
O God, we have one prayer to Thee:
That those few blind corrupt may see
The beauty of a peaceful world.

AUTUMN   Nina Mancuso

D a w n

The bronzed autumn hills,
Peer through misty mounds of haze,
The morning fog creeps in to capture
The splendor of nature's work of days.

N o o n

The glowing autumn noon day's ray,
Unmasks the leaves clothed in gypsy hue,
Reveals the sparkle of the country brook,
In whose mirror smiles the sky of blue.

N i g h t

The frost-tinged wind of autumn nights
Scatters the rainbows the trees threw down,
Sweeps them up with its mighty arm,
Hurling them like a prancing clown.

THE OCEAN OF LIFE   Jo Ann Stuard

The ocean of life is forever vibrant,
Always impelled by opposite forces;
Forever tormented, never still, life wavers.
In its jumble, life casts debris upon world's shores.

Fierce storms rage in life until, in anguish and throe,
It cires out, "O Master of Waters, hear my plea!"
And suddenly, a serene calm falls on troubled waters;
The tortured soul finds peace.

EVACUATION   Zuella G. Trende

Green leaves, turned to flame, blaze throughout
          the landscape.

Dancing winds, preparing to withdraw with
          the warm atmosphere, whirl off
          the stage setting.

Stately flowers, satisfied with their
          well-performed show, languish away
          for a winter vacation.

Autumn. The lingering departure of a carefree
          disconcern into a reflection of chilly
          welfare for the following era.

All these things are traditionally here; relieving
          the summer's cast before the icy fingers
          of winter bring down the final curtain.

ECHOES   James Anderson

A butterfly flounced upon a marigold
Murmuring, "The world is so wonderful."

A bumble bee, heavy with pollen,
Buzzed past and hummed,
"The world is so wonderful."

The summer rains tapped on my window,
"The world is so wonderful."

Far from home, but really close,
A bomb cried out,
"The world be damned."

COLOURED RAIN   Ruth Zweig

Prismatic points slapped wet on the pane,
Stained, and ran off, white and plain.
I searched for the sky, in this black city night,
And saw only rain, catching raw city light.
Bright and scintillant, intense and rich,
It poured down from nowhere so quick to bewitch.
It frosted the glass into cloudy opaque,
Dimmed all its colours to a crystalline wake.
Lightning flashed on a shady street
And the colours flew down in a silver sheet.
The rainbows froze, made a slicing sound,
As I lost my beauty in a sleeting pound.

AUTUMN'S SACRIFICIAL OFFERING
                                    Betty Jean Robertson
Along about this time every year,
Dogwood berries begin to appear.
Drops of blood with nails speared through;
Even the leaves blood-spattered too.
In the spring, the white cross was there
On the dogwood tree, bent with care.
Each corner nail dented, with dried blood brown;
In the center the thorns which were His crown.
The tree is small, and bent low with shame
Because our Jesus on it was slain.
To beg forgiveness, each year this tree
Brings forth gifts to keep alive His memory.

DUSK   Shirley Mae Oliver

        The sunshine melts
'mid purple   haze
            Beyond the western rim,
            And leaves the world
a cold, dark place
            With shadows gray and dim.

        Small lights appear
from everywhere;
            Small children lightly pass;
            A million silver stars
come out
            With pearls in dewy grass.

EVOLUTION   Vivian Johnson

Revealing
The red of many sunsets
The purple of early dawns
The silver of the moon rise
And
The sparkle of the stars
- - - - - - - - - -
The flaming log.

THE PAINT BRUSH   Theodora Foster

Oh, what the paint brush can create,
When some talented hand its motions dictate.
It can catch the softness of a new spring day,
It can catch the glee in children's play.
It glorifies each ray of the setting sun,
It shows the smoothness of a horse's run.
It captures the excitement of a gay dance floor,
The blue of heather on an English moor.
It portrays the vivid colors in the flaming fire,
The imaginative form of our Heavenly supplier.
What wonders of nature a brush can create,
When the hand of an artist, its motions dictate.

LEAF   Bing Kan Jew

Out of spring - green
        Grasses and trees
Along on the streets
        And stream.

Out of night - light,
        Moon and stars,
Hang on the sky
        And shine

Out on the world - time,
        Youth is gone,
Old leaves are tired,
        They drop on the streets.

Out of dead ashes -
        Life again!

THE AFTERNOON OF A FAUN   Frank H. Musial

What was living and fresh and verdant
Has now shriveled into deserts of sand, parched solitude bare.
And here I in this waste lie. From the radio drifts
Stokowski - Afternoon of a Faun - from that radio there.
Yet those strains no water, no oasis bring to the void.

Only a mirage . . .

In the theatre we sit; the ballet below
So amusing. The man wears a tiny, false tail.
The tall, beautiful lady he starts and she flees
And you smile. "What's a nymph?" I ask after the show.

. . . Only a mirage

Later I too, impetuous, I in mad youth's
Trifling folly, a goddess alarm
And, you gone,
What was living and fresh and verdant
Has now shriveled into deserts of sand, parched solitude bare.
And here I, in this waste, I caress all I have left of you --
Just a thin veil of memory.

SLEEP   James Hall

When night removes the tarnished bits of golden day
And smooths the sunset scars with silken fingertips,
The weary soul, within a world of silences,
On tip-toe treads the sloping path to sleep.

PRICELESS GIFTS   Marcia Nelson

There's beauty in the summer sun,
And magic in its light;
Enchantment in the silvery glow
Of moon and stars at night.
The laughter in a baby's eyes
Holds love and wealth untold;
For these are miracles which come
To folks both young and old.
The gifts which God alone can bring
Are those which can't be sold.
These things which money never buys
Are finer gifts than gold.

CAN'T UNDERSTAND IT   Nancy Ross

When Dad made fence and his thumb he did hit,
He said a word he shouldn't've, he had to admit.
Mom was washin', the clothes line broke,
That word had almost become a joke.
A little later, when brother was at play,
He pinched his finger and that word did say.
And he got his mouth washed out with soap,
But Mom didn't 'cause she said it about the broken rope;
Nor did Dad, when he hit his thumb fixin' fence.
You know, it really isn't fair and doesn't make sense,
I don't know why Mom and Dad should scold and shout;
Gee Whiz, sometimes it just slips out!

RETURN   Lois Myra Katz

The air was cold.
The pavements shrank from it;
The houses shrugged more deeply
Into surrounding foliage.
Street lamps shed indifferent light
Upon empty streets.

Homes held their warmth within them;
Until
I came to one.
Its windows gave light
That made a haze of all the rest.
Its door bid me welcome,
And I was home.

COLORS   Sylvia Jean Market

Brown are the mountains
    Blue are the skies
Green are the meadows
    where the oriole flies
White are the houses
    along the street
Yellow and blue
    are the Dutch houses neat.
Red are the tulips
    in quaint flowerbed,
As breezes pass by
    each nods its head.

TIME   Susan Seidner

We struggle on, and grovel for
Tomorrow's far evasive shore,
And in this unattractive way,
We carelessly form yesterday.

THE HUNTER   Billy Earl Wallace

There stalks the wary hunter,
Moving like a whisper of evil through the silent forest,
The lust to kill written on his face
In sullen, foreign lines.
Listen! - - -
There is a sound of fur against the bark,
In the thick jack pines appears the rack of a
majestic elk,
Then like a bolt aimed by Jupiter
The elk is gone - - -
The hunter shouts an oath.
Then there is peace.

AWAKENING   Lola Haight

I saw bright leaves drift slowly down,
I saw a woods swept bare
Of all its leafy summer clothes --
And knew that Fall dwelt there;

I saw cold, circling, swirling snow
Cover all the earth,
And heard Winter's dead silence
Broken but by North Wind's mirth;

I slogged through mud, while dreary rain
Poured down from leaden skies,
And asked my heart if God forgot
To tell the sun to rise --

But today I saw a meadow flower,
I heard a robin sing,
A soft breeze brushed against my face
And whispered low, "'Tis spring."

NIGHT WORLD   Willard Sakiestewa, Jr.

The sun after a day's journey finally disappears,
And Darkness creeps through the deep forest,
While over the tree tops a cold moon appears.
The stars of the heavens twinkle like diamonds.
Birds fly from tree to tree seeking a place for rest.
The wisest of them all has just begun his weird hoots.
The night world becomes a sleeping world to men.
But our world regardless of the darkness never dies.

SONNET   Mara Louise West

The fear that rides with every man on earth,
And haunts each trembling soul as though a ghost,
Is masked with pride that has no end, no mirth,
And comes without a warning to the host.
Its quiet step comes slowly without rest,
To dwell within one's bosom till his death.
Within our hearts we know we should protest,
We, with anxious eyes and quickened breath.
The day that we get rid of all our fear,
We'll be with Him upon another shore;
And it with us shall never more appear,
And we shall have no trouble of the fore.
Let's not let fear lead us away from Him
And we will have a life worth any gem.

SUNDAY MORNING   Myrtle Anne Cooper

Sunday is a happy day,
A day of quiet rest --
A time to pause upon my way
To think of how I'm blest.

As I walk along to God's house,
Somehow the beauty I see
Renews my strength - and I renounce
All evil thoughts in me.

Thank You, God, for this Sabbath Day;
Help me always to be true,
Walking along life's pathway
May I faithfully "follow through."

ELVES   Marie T. Szmabelanczyk

Tall trees swayed, in the glorious fall,
In answer to the elves' soft call.
It was so quiet and serene,
That I thought this must be a dream.

I wish that I could be like they,
Go whispering throughout the day.
But then, what would my mother think
To see an elf around the sink.

WHO KNOWS?   Marcille Rapp

What does it matter the color of man?
Their fate is the same in the Master's Hand.
It matters not whether black or white
They both see the stars that shine in the night.
But there is prejudice!

We will treat them the same, yellow, brown, or red.
Each needs food, clothes, a roof over his head.
Each must have God, and a friend in need
To help him, regardless of race or creed,
Why is there prejudice?

NOVEMBER   Sarah Anderson

November's here, when autumn leaves fall;
Her chilly breezes to winter do call.
November! then comes cold December;
Then Autumn is gone.

November's here with its reds and browns,
Football, frost, and pumpkins around;
November! then comes icy December;
Then Autumn is gone.

In November the Thanksgiving feast begins;
In November there are football games to win;
November! then comes bitter December;
Then Autumn is gone.

November will come again next year
Though at her passing fall sweet tears.
November! then comes bleak December;
Then Autumn is gone.

THE SHINING SUNBEAMS   Fuchsia Pettigrew

I love the shining sunbeams that set
    the world aglowing,
For me they almost seem to stop
    the wintry winds from blowing
They wake the sleeping flowers
    and lift their drowsy heads.
They help the merry, tuneful birds
    to build their wee, small nests.
I think that God in His love is meaning,
When He sends the sunshine gleaming,
To help and cheer us all the day
While we work and while we play.

WORK   Bob Jones

What fire is to the crucible;
What lightning is to the air;
What rain is to vegetation;
Work is, to human care.

He who will not work
Has lost his greatest chance
To balance mind and body
And further his advance.

He who works, does not steal,
But gets his fair reward,
In earthly blessings and mental peace,
And gains and holds man's high regard.

REFLECTIONS IN RAIN   Marcia Lampton

I walk along the somber streets
And on my face the raindrops beat.
Persistently they fall on earth
As if to hasten Spring's rebirth.

Look! Up above, a bird of red,
A sign of winter gone ahead,
Scarlet in a liquid sky --
Rise, my spirit, with it fly!

Oh gentle rain, erase away
The tribulations of the day;
And as you touch the barren sod,
I hail thee! Servant of my God.

OBEDIENCE   Suzanne Castellini

What is more exciting
Than to see black storm clouds fighting,
And the angry winds come racing through the trees?

When the heav'ns are torn asunder
Is it the roaring of the thunder
Or the light'ning flashes playing tag with Sound?

The bellows and dark looks are fun,
While the battle's a bloodless one.
Violent Nature, though unthinking, bows to its Law.

GIVE ME TOMORROW   Anna Marie Cavazos

Blazing sun has set; day's labor is done.
In my attic chamber and down below
All is quiet; all is peace -
Now to sleep and ready for tomorrow.

"Today may have been all the tomorrows, "
The peace and quiet whisper. And up above
What if --- ? Will it be all fleecy clouds,
Golden harps, delicate rainbows, and love?
Give me tomorrow, for a day's labor isn't enough.

SUNLIGHT   Sue Wall

Sleepy sun,
Enfolding me in a burning blanket of contentment,
Caressing me with tender fingers,
And probing into hidden depths,
Soothes and comforts me.

I rise
And passing into shadow,
Lose the clinging warmth and comfort of the blanket,
Gone -
Regained only by a new day and return.

And so I lost his love.
I left,
Shunning its protectiveness.
But unlike the sleepy sun,
Return will not regain it
Nor can it shine again.

THE MARKS OF TIME   Dave Goodman

Do not hide the marks of Time --
The travail and suffering of years,
No matter how and where I climb,
Your face, your smile, the bitter tears
Shine within my eyes and give me strength
To strive, to endure, to find new ways,
In spite of the troubles of life and death
That mar and twist and darken our days.

PSALM OF PEACE   David Kendall

We strive for peace and stretch our hands each way,
To grasp those hands that over oceans lay.
We loan our money, the riches of our land -
We send them soldiers, a vigil guard to stand.
Our people ship each package marked for Care,
To help each country in its task to bear.
Our life's blood shed upon their distant shores,
A nation's strength that we shall know no more!
What do we ask for this great sacrifice?
How can we look for them to pay the price?
Can we accept their debt as friends? We cry,
"Oh yes; for strength of nations we must try!
Oh yes; a flag of truce we all must fly!
Oh yes; for peace on earth, we'll fight and die!"

SONNET OF THE BLIND   Naomi R. Jammer

The world is swiftly spinning toward its doom.
Hate closed his door, and we are locked within;
Here we must perish in terror and sin,
Nations are cloaked in an atomic gloom
And suddenly, for Peace, there is no room.
Mark well the devil's silent, wicked grin;
He knows this bloody battle he will win,
He knows that man's power will vanish soon.
In history, the mighty Romans fell,
And future books shall tell of long crushed men,
Or rather beasts who lived in a steel spell.
We must stop this tide and carefully mend
Our ways, for if we don't, a life of hell
Will belong to us when we reach the end.

NIGHT   Kay Fleenor

I've often watched and wondered how the night
Steals silently across the earth and sky,
And in a cloak of black enshrouds the earth
With her dark folds. Then one by one with grace
And love, and care, she calls her host of stars
To peep beneath her folds and crown the night.
With long, thin hands that cast a silv'ry light
She lifts the breezes through her long, black hair,
And then, because the fast approaching dawn
Is breaking through her velvet cloak of black,
She gathers up her royal robes with care
And steals away with swiftness out of sight.

CANTICLE OF STEEL   Bonnie Bukolt

Praise and glory are Thine, O Lord,
For all the products of steel.
From great, majestic bridges
To simple, humble wheel;
From trains, and cars, and planes,
And roads, and railroad tracks,
To doorknobs, bolts, and nails,
And even hammer and tacks;
From powerful machinery
To appliances that shine;
Be given praise and glory,
All, O God, are Thine.

THE UNKNOWN ONE   Jean Ann Katz

Here he lies, the Unknown One,
He who is my brother, my father, my son.
Here he lies, picked from many, not few
He who is Protestant, Catholic, or Jew.
Here he lies, dark headed or light,
He whom we sent to fight our fight.
Here he lies, here in this grave
He who was strong, courageous and brave.

Here he lies, the Unknown One,
He who was once happy, full of fun.
Here he lies, brown-eyed or blue,
He who to his country forever was true.
Here he lies in this honored grave
He who was fighting for his country to save.
Here he lies, forgotten never
He whom we shall remember forever.

AFTER A DAY IN CENTRAL PARK   Sandra (Andree') Davis

A day and a dream -
The day is infinitely the dream,
And the dream forever the day.
        Here and there lie shadows
        And more to come.
Yet I know we live all in a dream
        And there is forever no end
And forever no beginning for us.

ADAPTABLE   Arlene Marie Hess

A hairpin fills a woman's needs,
As no other object will.
If you need repairs on anything,
This gadget fills the bill.

It really is just dandy
For tightening up a screw,
But to women who are handy,
This use is nothing new.

To say that's all it's good for,
It really is not fair,
For when it has no other use,
She puts it in her hair.

WARNING OF THE CLOCK
                    Michael Dougherty
Tick-tock-tick-tock
    hear the solemn, foreboding clock.
In its own stolid way
    Perpetually it will say:
        Get to work!

It tells me now is when,
    now over studies I should bend,
If I didn't put it off,
    all my worries I could doff,
        And be free.

This says he,
Oh, as bluntly as can be,
    and he says it audibly,
In his tick-tocking way
        of telling me.

SILHOUETTES   Roberta Maier

Dark oozes the blood to the virgin white
The pulse of life it comes to be,
The mind flashes a speck of light
To show the soul of man in serenity,
Memories willfully crowd the hour
That are not yet lost in the realm of the past,
They bring to the present a sense of power
That rules the fervor that will forever last,
Long fall the darkened shadows to the golden dawn
They reap in the mystic dreams of man,
In a moment of truth, they are suddenly gone
They seem to flee like a wavering fan,
Memories, shadows, all the things man can forget
Return to the mind in the deepened pulse of a silhouette.

TWENTIETH CENTURY   Elizabeth Barkins

"Let live, " the weakened cry,
"Let feast, " the mighty roar,
Wealth will vanish by and by
And poverty reign forever more.

Again the world is back at war,
Again death firmly grips a hold,
Few are left to cross the door
To peace, that never once grows old.

TO A STAR   Mary Brennan

Oh star that lights a dream for me
    Of life and love and ecstacy
That points the way where angels glide
    Across the night draped trackless sky.

Star that marks our Savior's birth
    Beaming God's love from Heaven to Earth
And shines on a manger wherein lies
    A sleeping babe, under His mother's tender eyes.

Star that shines in the sky tonight
    Keep my pathway clear and bright
So that when my life shall come to end,
    I, my knee, may also bend.

CRYSTAL GAZING   Joan Parlee

There are times when we think of the future,
    As a pleasant time to come,
A time to play, and eat, and sleep,
    And have some wonderful fun.

And then, there are times in the depths of despair,
    When we think with a heavy heart,
Of the future black and gloomy,
    But this really isn't smart.

If you should take to crystal gazing,
    Look on the bright side of the ball,
At the fun, the frolic, and the peace,
    That can be had by us all.

PRAYER   Marilyn Moore

Into the world of night I pour my thoughts:
Of love and hope, and hate for things unknown -
Of God; and then an old familiar phrase
Returns, to bring with armth and tenderness
My answer, in sweet words of old and near -
Forgotten sage; my heart is full and tears
Trace down my cheeks a path of silver light
Highlighted by the moon, that waits in prayer,
As I - my head bowed low in homage small
To One who made us both - the moon and me -
Gives me the strength to raise again my head,
Repeats with me the lines that once were all
And all to me: "Hallowed be thy name."

WAR CHANT   Clement Masloff

I sing of modern and ancient warriors
Who never knew why they died;
Who rushed into battle to slaughter the foe,
To fight for their foolish pride.

They never were told the reason why
They suffered, they starved, and grieved;
Who cared if they understood the Cause?
Who asked them what creed they believed?

There must be a Camp Eternal
Where beaten soldiers can go
To rest from their bloody battles
After the death and the woe.

WAR   John J. Miller

Men have strived to stop it
But none have yet succeeded;
Others have died waging it
But, alas, have died in vain --
It has prevailed since the beginning
Because states were divided in thought;
It will prevail to the end
Because man is unlikely to learn.

AMBITION   Alan Fuller

I shall not bow to any man,
No tyrant's subject shall I be,
No king will rule the life I spend,
No queen will force me to my knee.

To be a king shall be my aim;
To reap awards and win acclaim;
To share in laughter, not in tears,
To be pampered, not made poor by years.

But though a lofty life I spend,
I shall remember this --
No man should be too proud to bend,
Or happiness he'll miss.

AFTER THE RAIN   Alice Kenney

The sun peeks through the leaden clouds;
Its golden rays slant toward the ground.
They shine on roofs of houses near
And gleam from all the puddles round.

The children run from every house;
Their gaiety is joy to see.
The morning's dreary rain is past;
The sun has come to set them free.

At last the spring twilight descends;
The children slowly leave the street.
The town has had its latest bath
And goes to sleep, all clean and neat.

ROADS   Christine Harris

Like lonely wanderers, they meander through
Peaceful valleys covered with carpets of grass,
Through dark, shady forests with trees standing like sentries
Keeping watch over the young of the forest.

They wind through the jungles of darkest Africa,
Making a perilous path for those who dare to follow;
But sometimes, in a kind way, serving as a beacon to the lost.

Then, turning into giant Milky Ways, they ramble over hills,
Weaving among forests and valleys,
Speeding across vast, barren plains;
A seemingly never-ending network of ribbon,
Making up roads - the international guide.

CIVILIZATION   John Percy

Who, I ask,
Is really civilized?
The Bushman
Peaceful in his hut?
The Hindu
Tending his rice fields?
Or the white man
Sowing destruction
Throughout the world?

DREAM THOUGHTS   Mary Chris Sideris

Compare the words I dream about
With those my pen does write,
Those in my mind, without a doubt,
Are words that do excite.

Yet seldom do they come by day,
It's always past midnight,
With paper, pen, all put away,
And all's locked out of sight.

The words I dreamt - so eloquent,
Hurry - at once to write!
Alas, they were magnificent,
But written late, they're trite.

TRANSFORMATION   Patricia Pfaff

Life is a crazy concoction of things!
I was like a bat flying aimlessly through dark, musty caves,
Showing myself only at night;
But then a phantom appeared on one dark, dreary night.
And I --
I was turned into a lovely butterfly
With extravagant, multicolored wings
Which travels among the most beautiful of flowers.
And I --
I have discovered I can land on anything I wish.

DEATH COMES TO GAIL MALMSHEIMER
Gail Malmsheimer

Misty blackness swirls around me.
I am helpless.
Powerless to move, to think, to speak,
To cry out in my desperation.
Alone in a dark, somber world,
I search vainly for a light in the blackness;
But there is none.
Suddenly I realize that Death is mine.
I am no longer afraid.
Afraid of not breathing, not moving, not thinking,
Afraid of an unknown fear.
I am one of a legion of many --
Caught in an eternal sleep.

WHY   Jim Klingsporn

It's strange, it's odd, it's peculiar,
It's so futile that it's funny,
That of the things men value most,
They try to buy with money,

They cannot purchase love nor life,
Nor joy with all their gold,
Nor can they buy a character,
That is just and bold.

Nor when they reach that last great Court,
Where their verdict shall be given
They'll find that all their money
Still won't buy their way to heaven.

TIME   Charles Near

Snow will come, but snow must go,
Rain may fall, the wind may blow,
Old trees die and new ones grow,
          But time goes marching on.

Slowly, surely, lifetimes pass;
Youth turns aged, like withered grass.
Accomplish now, for all too fast
          Will time go marching on.

SEASON'S BOND   William Owen Anderson

Summer green through purple veil,
Hills and vales their shapes prevail,
On sunny morn or humid night,
For snows and winds are still in flight.

Winter haze through grey-white veil,
Hills and vales their shapes prevail,
O'er snowy banks on mornings white,
God shows His strength in winter might.

Lacy white floats through the blue,
Ocean's green and amber hue
Commends a Power so strong and good,
That man is bound in brotherhood.

AND YET THEY SAY   David Yolton

Above the clouds, stretching toward the heavens
Above the swiftly flowing streams,
Beyond the verdant pastures, the prairies,
Far surpassing the hills and rolling plains,
Beyond the lowlands, hued in green,
Above the timberline and fields of flowers;
Above all this is still the best.
With royal ermine robes of glistening snow,
In greatest splendor, finest dignity,
All the poise and beauty a thing could possess:
The tallest mountain in the world;
Chimborazo, the mighty, towers above the rest
A living memorial to our God.
And yet some say "There is no God!"

A SILENT RECORD   Harriet V. Coel

Trees find joy on my ground;
Birds have companionship and homes on site;
Sun bright skies, sometimes clouds floating around;
By night the big moon baby sitting a star.
I do for others and take what they can give;
Friendship afresh and some renewed from afar.
I am just a silent record that plays memories;
My autograph for diaries - A Summer Camp.

CONTRAST   Joan Van Krevelen

It is a cold, a crisp, a cheerless night.
The street is stark with dirty snow and ruts.
The wind cuts foggy figures with the light,
And in its path a ghostlike creature struts.
The cinders form a pattern with the grease
And stripes made deep by tracks of many wheels.
It's here the creature stalks with little peace.
The harshness of a cruel world he feels.
He turns and starts from this to a side street
And stops! A hush has overcome the land.
The once-black crystals now are clear and fair
And its pure white has not been marred by feet.
A quiet calm reigns just as if His hand
Had touched the land and left His presence there.

THE SEA OF LIFE   Glenda Jane Parsons

Out on the Sea of Life we roam
Without knowledge of what's before
Rocking on huge waves and foam
Waiting for a glimpse of a shore.

But alas! A shore is not in sight
Until our life's journey is o'er
And we have tried with all our might
To reach that far, successful shore.

The years we've spent doing our best
Have been a struggle, first to last
But we'll be happy with the rest
Who've sailed the Sea of Life full mast.

SELF DETERMINATION   Margaret Eliot

Thus life's desire is for determination,
For wrong and right ----, is matter of desire
To travel onward without hesitation
From man's own heart comes the compelling fire.

The inevitable end comes of man's own creation,
From hearts to lips comes his astonished cry
As self-built paths come to their termination
And man must die.

SPRING NIGHT   Pat Moss

The night is soft and wispy
Like a gown of finest lace;
Drifting from sky to earth,
Touching all with scented embrace.

Fluorescent clouds and misty moon,
The glow of twinkling, gem-like stars,
Are night's glistening, precious jewels
As she covers daylight scars.

The rustling sounds are music
To a still and listening ear;
The notes are shaped and floating
As the wispy lace draws near.

SIMIAN SUGGESTION   Margaret Tschiffely

Did you ever stop to think,
As with loathing you recall
That the monkey's uncle
Might really be your pa?
That the monk
Might also think,
With loathing of his unk,
Of what a fool he was
And what fools we are -
Always fighting someone's war
Always landing on someone's shore?
He looks at this bungle
Of so called civilization,
"Why not try the jungle,"
He happily drools,
"Oh, cousins, you fools!"

HAVE YOU HEARD THE WHISPER OF A LONELY NIGHT?

Charlotte A. Trolenberg

Have you heard the whisper of a lonely night,
When the moon reveals itself through a golden cloth?
The wind like a young and listless bird flies through the trees
Gently touching each tiny branch.

The troops of grass sway together with a homesick wind,
Stirring so easily, not wanting to wake nature.
I helplessly look to the sky for guidance;
Then a friendly star beams down to me its undaunted security.

APRIL SONNET   Tom Cox

At last the mountains show their summer lines
As now no snowy blankets on them lie.
No frigid winds do shake the stately pines
And icy cold no more the fields does ply.
Gone are the chilling blasts, gone winter's signs
Again the grass stabs upward to the sky,
Once more the sun with summer's glory shines
As geese their solemn northward path do fly.
The trials of the winter are forgot
When life and love return North once again,
Yet fear and death and wanting are but naught
If you can only face them with a grin.
Yes, even when your sun in clouds is caught
Send out its radiant beams and say, "I'll win."

COME FORTH FUTILE ONES   Jimmie Hopper

Stench filled pit of fate,
Lures him by his useless hate.
Over the paths of distress,
Desiring but an amorous caress.
On, on as he journeys on,
Endless toil of the bone.
Downtrodden peasant, rise to your feet,
Get the reward due your worthless meat.
Grasp thy praise and honor dear,
'Tis but the worth of wasted tears.
Surroundings of years never yours,
Only the fear of the government couriers.
Bursting soul and heart of thine,
Break those shackles, now is the time.

SPEAK GENTLY   Eloise Rose

Speak gently, Spring, and make no sudden sound;
For in my winding garden yesterday I found
New-born flowers popping up from the ground -
                Speak gently

Walk softly, March, forbear the bitter blow;
The flowers head within a blossom, they blossom above the snow
The group of flowers saw their blossom go --
                Walk softly

Go lightly, Spring, oh give them an alarm;
When you covered them with Mother Nature to shelter them from harm
The flowers so beautiful in my arm -
                Go lightly

Step softly, March, with your rough hurricane;
Covering one another and bowing with pain
The beautiful flowers are glowing in the rain -
                Step softly.

AWAK'NING   Janet Mae Hardy

The young dawn casts her first pink ray
Upon the wak'ning earth:
An early-bird with song bursts forth
To herald a new day-s birth:
The red-gold bars of Heaven
Become the handmaids of the sun
Who veil the morning star
And bid their queen to come.

LOST LOVE   Mary Caryl Broadhead

I yearned to love so I made you mine,
Set my heart within your hands,
Made you better than you were,
Built a man that I could love,
Gave you starry-eyed perfection.

But Time ends the sweetest dreams
And opens wide the blindest eyes.
Someday I'll find another love
For I was certainly born to care.
Someday I'll look back and laugh,
But not now -- now I'll cry.

DAWN AND THE BAYOU   Sarah Jones

The thin mist rises from the silent black waters.
Tall reeds whisper to the wind.
Long gray beards show the great age
Of the gnarled cypress bent to look in the deep depths.
The lilies, yellow gold, are set as jewels
In the dark green swamp ivy crown
Along the bank.
A white egret circles above
And lands on the shallow bar
To stand statue-like; pretending to sleep.
From the towering magnolia trees
The dew studded blossoms glisten
When touched by tiny rays of light
Streaming through the waxy, emerald leaves.
The sun rises above the horizon
Bringing the new day.
Thus is dawn on the Bayou.

TO A CORSAGE   Helen Smith

You, Miss Lilac,
          Were my corsage,
You, pinned close to my heart,
          Made my graduation complete
You, lovely in your gown of lilac,
          Felt the tingling thrill
You, only you
          Will ever know my joy.

WINTER   Jacklyn Kimberlin

I'm coming to cover the country,
I'll touch all the windows with frost,
I'll kiss all the pine trees with snowdrops,
I'll put on a show without cost.

I'll freeze all the ice ponds for skating,
I'll paint all the round little cheeks,
I'll tuck all the bears into hiding
Where they will sleep soundly for weeks.

Sometimes when I'm through for the day,
I realize I'm weary and cold;
I wish for a while that I could play
With summer without being bold.

THE NEEDLE   Jean Hendrickson

Groping for tomorrow
I stumbled over the past --
And
Lost
All
Hope
Of ever finding today
In the strawstack of life.

MIRACLE   Janice Riley

A lacework of silvery threads,
Arranged in a mystic design,
Spun of moonbeams and dew,
By Nature, the weaver devine!

A soft, white puff of silk
To a brown twig bravely clings,
Enclosing the essence of life,
Awaiting the birth of free wings.

Fabrics so fragile, yet strong --
A miracle surely is this --
In the delicate web of the spider
And the butterfly's chrysalis

SIGNS OF AUTUMN   Rebecca Baggett

Now is the time for signs of fall -
Ripening apples in trees so tall;
Granaries filled with wheat and rye;
Flocks of birds flying so high;
Trees half-bare of colorful leaves;
Golden pumpkins 'round corn sheaves;
Purple grapes weighting the vine;
Milkweed floating - fiber fine;
Insect orchestras filling the air;
Rich brown nuts lying everywhere;
Sunrise clouded by smoke-like haze;
Colder mornings, shorter days.
O, happy Autumn, rich and rare,
God's bountiful love is everywhere!

TWO PRAYERS   Diana Ludwick

A homely swan in a pond one day
Lifted his head and began to pray;
"Lord, make me graceful and proud, is my plea,
That by all other fowls I envied might be."

There was also a deer on that very day,
Whose whispered prayer began in this way:
"Lord, make me swift and alert, is my plea,
That all other creatures will honor me."

And then in a field very far away,
A beautiful tree began to pray:
"Lord, let me grow to be strong, is my plea,
So I may give honor and glory to Thee."

The good Lord on His throne above
Felt sad, for in two prayers there was no love,
So He gave His blessing to the tree,
And let it cradle His Son on Calvary.

WIND"S SONG   Betty Freeto

The wind is the harp of the angel of God
It plays a varied tune;
It drones a dirge to a dying fall,
Or sings a hymn to the moon.

In winter it drums a warrior's cry
With fearful banshee shriek;
In spring - the joyous song of relief,
From the chains of a winter bleak.

In summer the harpist restrains himself
To a quiet, lethargic day,
Then fashions a song of the love of life
And the glorious midsummer day.

REVERIE   Andrea Stelle

While basking on the purple sands,
My thoughts move on to distant lands.
Where red flamingoes dip their beaks
In placid ponds the twilight seeks,
And brown gazelles in play do leap,
While near the trees the shadows creep.
Then from my reverie I wake,
Reluctantly my dreams forsake.

DOOMED MELODY   Fydelis Witt

The haunting refrain goes ragingly on
To grasp you, where'er you may be;
The music so mystic, reluctant to greet
Capture, the human's wide sea.

Refrains so dreamy, joyful, serene,
Are raging throughout each mind,
To someday be chosen and wasted away,
By one so musically blind.

WHY?   Irene Fink

Why the beauty of flowers in spring?
          Why the patterned flakes of snow?
Why the various birds to sing?
          Because God made it so.

Why wholesome work and healthy play?
          Why do the rivers flow?
Why do we have night and day?
          Because God willed it so.

Why are people filled with hate?
          Why are death notes made to blow?
Why are we fearful of our fate?
          Because w e made it so!

FROM FALL TO WINTER   Joan C. Swanson

The leaves are falling, brown and red
Upon the earth, once fresh and green
In garden bare, they'll make their bed
Blown there by fall winds, sharp and keen.

The flowers - almost all are gone
Their petals dropping, one by one
Their colors fading, as the lawn
Grows brown, awaiting winter sun.

The birds fly southward, sure and swift
To winter homes, they left last spring
The winds will blow, the snow will drift,
The Christmas bells so soon will ring.

UNCHANGEABLE   Jean Hogan

When leaves of gold and scarlet hue
Descend to kiss
The Earth,
When softly whirling flakes of snow
Caress the bending
Boughs,
When gentle drops of welcome rain
Proclaim that spring is
Here,
Let glad hearts know
That through the seasons change
God's love is still the same.

NIGHT MUSIC   Kay Ent

Jazz --- and the night breathes a song -
Melancholy, hauntingly, it floats through the night,
Triumphantly it reigns over the darkness.
It is King.

From the lighted house comes blues -
A singer --- a song.
The cry of a trumpet,
Footsteps of a drum.

Lazily it weaves through the night.
Now it has stopped -
The house is dark -
Blackness crawls onto its throne to rule once again.

QUERY   John Ferren

Though March comes in like a lion,
And then departs like a lamb,
It's hard to believe
And I can't quite conceive
How a lamb could induce
Or so much confuse,
That lion, - so that he would leave.

And so replaced,
Thus greatly disgraced,
Our lion must wait for next year,
When he enters the realm
And stays at the helm
'Til replaced by the smaller inferior.

BAY OF BISCAY   Sheila Mace

The mighty ball of orange fire rose to greet the clear blue sky,
Rose o'er purple Spanish mountains,
Hazy in the morning light.

The rolling, roaring, golden breakers crashing on the shore beneath
Rushed to meet the rising sun, who
Glinted on the endless sea.

The fragile, fairy, sand-grown grasses wavered in the morning breeze,
Basking in the gen'rous warm light
Pouring from the sun above.

NIGHT IN THE CITY   Joan Kiggins

Lights in the city -
Diamonds on black velvet.
Neon signs -
Rainbows in the sky.
Headlights -
Cat's eyes in the darkness.

Streets cluttered with theater crowds,
Taxis - bees swarming
With horns playing a finale
To another night in the city.

THE MOON MAID   Mary Valandingham

Diana, you stand there
          Clothed all in white,
Moon Maid of wonder,
          Herald of delight.

Diana, you stood there
          Centuries gone by,
When you loved one and left him
          There with a sigh.

Diana, you'll stand there
          For worlds yet to come,
Daughter of Darkness,
          Sister of Sun.

TABLOID   Layton Fireng

The sun comes up, and a rooster crows;
  A late man gulps his coffee, a baby cries;
  The subway rattles, and church bells ring;
No one knows where he is, or where he is going,
But any newspaper will tell you where he has been.

IT'S MORNING   Vesta Bailey

   I love the silent early world
   Flooded in the first sunshine;
   With the houses all sleeping
   Just like the end of time.

   I love the fragrance of the flowers;
   They seem so extra sweet.
   I love the feathery breezes then
   It is so hard to beat.

   With only the birds flitting
   From tree to tree to sing.
   I love to see the earth then
   In the early morning.

ALONE AND AFRAID   Paul Kearney

   The Past is a memory ...
   The Future, a dark hallway.
   I hesitate to cross
   That threshold of mystery.
   Not afraid of the dark
   Nor worried about myself
   But humans are not really
   My chosen companions.

   Living is not hard
   For such people as me.
   No intricate paths
   No problems of life;
   And at the end of the hall
   There's a bright light of hope.
   But humans are really
   My chosen companions.

   If I were alone,
   I could live in peace.
   It's these people about me
   Who bring all the grief.

FROM BOY INTO MAN   Barbara Anne Swindell

There's a man that I know, and he lives near you
            In a town called Everywhere;
You might not think he's a man from his hat
            Or the clothes he may chance to wear;
But under the jacket with many a patch
            Is a heart more precious than gold -
The heart of a man 'neath the coat of a boy,
            A man who is twelve years old.

We never may know what the future will make
            Of the boys that we carelessly meet,
For many a statesman is now at school,
            And presidents play in the street.
The hand that is busy with playthings now
            The reins of power will hold;
So I take off my hat and gladly salute
            This man who is twelve years old.

THE THINGS I SEE   Roslyn Morris

I go through life without much thought,
I look around with eyes and heart
The clean, green freshness of a field,
The dark, drab bleakness of a town,
But with this bleakness I find hope
For from the darkness light will appear
And on that day all life will start anew.

WHAT IS IT?   Frances Adams

Is it magic?
Does it move?
Is it really, truly there?
Do I see it?
Can I hear it?
Is it pulling at my hair?
Is it I?
Or is it you?
Do you see it dancing there?

There it is!
Now it's gone!
Oh, tell me, sister fair,
Is that a spirit on the wall
Or just the candle's flair?

ODE TO THE SEA   David Edwards

I stand on the edge of the sea,
And I wish that I were beneath the deep, grey waters,
Where I would eternally dance . . . .
And as I look,
I see my image in the surf,
And I feel an exultation,
For I wonder if, in reality, this reflection is not
That elusive and inexplainable being
That dances beneath the turbulent sea of my life:
That mysterious essence that is me,
That is my soul . . . .

LOVE   Ruth MacKenzie Barnes

Love is the warm pulsation of the earth,
Beating throughout all time unconsciously,
Vibrating noiselessly against the walls
Of the entire creation. Its harmony
Of movement glides within the dormant heart
And sets it glowing. Effervescent bursts
The spirit to the astral plane, a sun
Itself, celestial beauty unrestrained.
So, filled with love, that soul perhaps may touch
The secret of the universe and know
The ecstasy of earthly paradise.

WRETCHED RAIN   Marilyn Noesen

I walk in the rain
No living being nears me
My thoughts are on the petty things
          that trouble my selfish heart.
I see, in the distance, oblique buildings
The rain filters the fog that slumps on
          my soul.
The city's gray lights throw off an arc
          of dejection
I mumble a sad soliloquy to my
          inner self,
Which whispers back a low, stifled moan
I know no one who moves the fog
But God must have some Spirit o'er me
          that soothes my aching world.

TREE OF LIFE   Karen Marie Nissen

Life is like a tree bending its arms to the sky,
Until a storm when, with sadness,
It bends to earth with a sigh.
We are the leaves filled with gladness.

In the Spring of life you are young and gay,
You blossom with life so free;
In the Summer of life you're older and wiser,
And the years fade away like the sands of the sea.

In the Autumn of life you are wrinkled and old
Content to dream of days gone by,
In the Winter of life your heart beats slow,
And after this you fade and die.

Despair not, my lonely one,
A better life is yet to come!

INFIRMARY   Christine Richards

The alcoholed thermometer,
The crispness of the sheet,
The hissing of the radiator,
Donny's padded feet.

But to those infirmed and ill
The pungent smell of daffodil
Brings the welcome touch of spring,
Brittle, sweet.

AUTUMN   Larry Brown

The autumn is a pretty time,
Upon the sweet earth's breast;
When green leaves turn a golden brown,
And fall from trees to rest.

When God is in His heaven,
And we are on His earth,
When birds are in the fragrant air,
And the world's in harvest girth;

The sun - the moon - the stars -
Seem prettier than before -
Because it is the autumn time,
The time that I adore.

COWARDS   Virginia Palmer

A poem
Is a bit of a soul
Written down for the world to see.
Some poets, like me
Do not have the courage
To give the world their soul.
So they hide their poems,
In the backs of dusty desk drawers.

AN ILLUSTRATION OF DISSATISFACTION   Marti Ritzman

In winter, as the golden sun goes down,
When , by each soul, God's path of love is trod,
The greenness of the trees has turned to brown,
And each person pays homage to his God,
As sky colors reflect upon the snow
(They're in the snow themselves, it looks to be)
The tired workmen as they homeward go
This quiet summer memory brings to me;
I think of fruit borne on the green trees,
So precious is the blueness of the sky,
I see ships sailing upon the wide seas,
Of summer, thoughts return to my mind's eye.
To change the seasons is our great desire;
Another reason God's power we admire.

SPRING   Barbara Adams

Idle fancies of spring air
Come and go with little care.
Lover's thoughts; maid's young dreams
Are but fancies of Spring it seems.

Grass shoots up through the good brown earth
And brings one thoughts of Spring's rebirth.
Couples strolling hand in hand
Can be seen throughout the land.

Children playing in the park
Are sure signs of Spring's mark.
Songs of sweetness fill the air,
And there is happiness everywhere.

SONGS OF THE LOOMS   Nancy Eddie

The chattering looms
Are like talkative women
Arguing, gossiping
Murmuring to themselves.
They laugh and sob and weep.
They falter, quicken, then abate.
Ebbing and flowing as the restless sea.

The looms sing in clamorous harmony;
Their songs have all the joy,
The pain, the laughter and the sorrow
Of people who hoe - hoe - hoe, in burning sun
Of men who chop - chop - chop,
The hot green miles of cotton rows.

They sing of those who pick the snowy boles
The song of the dark skinned stevedores
Sweating, singing, rolling cotton down the river,
A thousand voices in one great chorus,
A blending of all notes into one great swinging harmony
This is the song of the looms.

YOU DON'T HAVE TO BE   Ruby Treadway

You don't have to be an artist
To appreciate the view
Of the glory of the sunset
And a dawn which bursts anew.

You don't have to be a poet
To love the valleys and the streams
You just have to have a heart full of love
And a pocket full of dreams.

MIND AND LIFE   David M. Zielonka

Solemnity is wise, they say,
But levity is also need;
A museful mind builds character,
A martinet is strong for deed.

So rare the perfect balance found,
Abnormal those few pseudonymed;
Unchancy, though, the fate of one
Whose mind, unbated, aspen trimmed.

SNOW AND MARCHING MEN   Howell Hardie

The snowflakes fell and nestled, fell and nestled.
Footsteps crunched or scuffed, but never tramped.
Words hung in air, vapor-like, dreading to fade.
The barracks rose unshivering, yet cold.
The parade-ground was a broad, white, velvety carpet,
                Strange path for marching men.
The cannon sat on their wheels 'neath cuddling snow.
Ensconsed beneath the Arch, seeing the ghostly trees
That etched the sky with silvery skeletons,
Hearing muffled steps and muted words,
I watched the nestling and cuddling, the nestling and cuddling
                Of the snow on marching men.

STEPS   Marilyn Schnur

An empty school is wonderful
        When the last bells for the day have run,
And everyone's gone, and the only sound
        Is the far off honking of swift passing cars;
And the ghostly sound of your own two feet
        As they go tramping along,
First right, then left
        In the rhythmic pacing of lonesome footsteps,
Across the school room floor toward the door -
        Then home.

THE BATTLE   Maudine Rambo

Fall has come and trees are getting sleepy,
They are longing greatly for winter beds,
Nor are they the least bit sad or weepy
At finding leaves are falling from their heads.
They know the leaves are falling to the ground
To protect their roots from the icy snow
That falls unceasingly since they have found
This way to guard themselves against this foe.
When Spring has come this battle they will win,
For down the river their enemy will run,
And all the trees will wake and bloom again
With water, and soil, and warmth from the sun.
Yes, this battle goes on year after year,
But the trees always win, so do not fear.

MAGIC   Dorothy Sawyer

I knew from the moment I stepped through the door
That things were different somehow.
The trees that had been so sullen and bare
Were decked in their finest now.
Where before there had been but a blanket of snow,
A velvet green carpet now lay.
The cold, bleak ground I had seen just before
Was now, by sweet flowers, made gay.
A wisp of breeze set the wood nymphs afoot,
And the trees did a bit of a dance.
For nature had sprinkled the magic of spring
And had left her whole world in a trance.

THE WITCHING HOUR   Wanda Harlowe

A full moon rides high tonight,
This magic night, this night for reminiscence.
Over all there is the hushed stillness of waiting,
With the town nestling in the valley between the hills.
The wind blows softly, bringing the fragrance of pine,
Of fresh new earth,
And the nostalgic smell of old and rotting wood.

Ah, this wind is a soft, sad wind,
A whispering and caressing wind.
It whispers secrets of long ago,
Secrets that can be told only at midnight
And its caresses are the long, sweet valedictions
Of the silver night.

CHILD OF THE WILD   Jack Larson

I was taught to run with the deer,
And the elk gave me his pride.
The mouse gave me his fear,
While the fox gave me his stride.

Oh, the owl gave me his wisdom,
And the bird gave me his song.
The stag gave me his kingdom,
And the bear taught me no wrong.

The moose gave me his power,
And the trout gave me his speed.
I loved the April shower,
And the rasping of the reed.

STORMY AUTUMN — Mary Davis

The rain was weeping forgotten tears,
And the wind moaned forgotten sighs
To a ghostly moon.
The trees shivered, and their leaves
Fell like memories through countless years.
I, too, shivered for I remembered
The tears, the sighs, the ache of a broken heart,
The quietness of death.

SONNET TO A WISE LITTLE BROOK — Carol Bush

A brook has many things that it could say
Of forest life that feeds on grass near there,
    Where graceful deer with it their secrets share.
A brook sees too the fawns aglow with play
    The brook yet quickly wends its merry way
And watches babies under watchful care,
    Their mothers often scenting quiet air.
The brook flows gently through a quiet bay
    With thoughts now straying over passing time,
The little brook is wise in ways of life
    And knows all the secrets nature keeps,
Observes that all the scheme of life has rhyme.
    The brook beholds a life which knows small strife,
And fullness gained from knowledge sweet, now reaps.

SUCCESS — Eileen Gillner

When earth above me mends where it was cracked
And my dead body lies beneath the sod,
Then will I be forgotten with the rest
Who once had lived, and loved, and feared a God?

Of fame and glory now I ask no part
And do not say that long since I have passed
The world will smile to speak and hear my name
Or my impression on it always last.

But if a soul for one thing that I've done,
Is not the better for the simple deed
Though fame should come to me if I have failed
To please my God, I could not then succeed.

THE RIFLE   Homer Miller

You, that are old and rusted,
You, that have held life and death within your barrel,
You, that have driven the plentiful game from the open fields
                    and the woods,
You, that have made widows and orphans,
You, that are death in the hands of greedy men,
You, that are a shame and disgrace to mankind,
What have you to say in defense of yourself?

SILVER RAIN   Chuck Schroeder

Where is an arrow sharp enough
Or a bullet straight to the mark
Or a thunderbolt that splits the sky
Or a blaze of lightning spark?
What can shatter that white storm cloud,
Split it and split it again -
And drench me, flood me, and cover me,
With a shower of silver rain?

DEFINITION   C. Elizabeth Milne

I asked a laughing streamlet
I questioned stars above
But now I kneel alone and pray
O Father, what is love?

A tender word, a moment sweet
One kiss and joy I knew not of?
A dream now shattered at my feet
O Father tell me, is this love?

A jealous worm deep in my heart
To reign where once ruled joy's sweet dove
An aching gloom within my soul
O Father tell me, is this love?

But then I think of joys once mine
Of how his lips were warm and sweet
I think of how his eyes would shine
And tender words that he'd repeat.

And as my answer comes to me
I whisper thanks to God above
"Have faith and hope and memory
And trust the Lord, for that is love."

THE ANSWER   Emily Scott

Death comes to all so we should love our life,
A life resplendent with a gift from Him
Above us all. Think not of loved ones lost
By hands of men, of battle smoke, of world
Unrest. For are we not God's own children
And life on earth is but a test of faith?

BEAUTY   Aileen Ristig

I saw her in the golden beams of sunlight
As they waken from sleep the yellow buttercups
In their dewy beds.

I felt her as the sun hovered
Over the earth in a blaze of seething
Red and gold.

I saw her as the sun descending
Crowned Day with turquoise, opal and amethyst
And welcomed Night.

I see her now as Night glides over earth,
Her blue-black velvet fringed with silver stars,
And paints my garden with the white light of a
Wondering moon.

OUR COUNTRY   Harriet Taussig

Florida:
Spanish moss reflected clear
In placid streams of blue and gold,
Timid fawn and graceful deer
Drink of the azure waters, cold.

California:
Snow-capped mountains upward reach
And disappear in milk-white clouds.
Drifting desert sands below
Gleam not; their glory mist enshrouds.

Arizona:
Mighty monuments of rock
Towering 'neath the turquoise skies,
Flashing colors, red and cold,
With windswept face the steep cliffs rise.

MUSIC   Shirley Harshbarger

There's music in the waters
   It dances in the lakes,
   Bubbles in the streams,
   Laughs at the waterfalls,
   And sings with the rain.

There's music in the evening time
   It comes from happy children,
   Twinkles from the stars,
   Skips with the wind,
   And jingles from the sleigh bells.

SNOWFALL   Marilyn Hunter

Snow is falling softly, gently,
Covering the earth with cotton fluff;
It drifts o'er the steeple of the slumbering church;
Then melts,
Leaving behind a path of tricking tears;
It plays hide-and-seek with the stars
And mimics twinkling prisms glimmering in the moonlight;
It flutters - a moving veil of white polka dots -
Against the black of night -
And the snow still falls to earth,
A mystic, sugary fairyland in the making.

WALKING ALONE   Jeanine Conn

Just to be alone with no one near,
No one to speak to; no one to hear.
For company, the wind whispering
   to a tree;
And a little song singing inside
   of me.

The crickets chirp; the night owl
   cries;
Every little care within me dies;
My heart is light and full of gladness.

There is no sorrow; there is no
   sadness.
Nor is there hatred or resentment
Just a night filled with peace and
   contentment.

OUR FATHER'S HOME Maureen Fitzhenry

There's a golden gate at the end of the road,
Through which each must pass alone;
Beyond the gate we find happiness and rest,
And comfort in the thought -
    That a loving God knows best.

THE LOVE OF PYGMALION Nancy Campbell

Pygmalion, the sculptor, had a rare
And wondrous gift. And yet, alas, the stone
He carved was warmer than his heart. Alone,
Austere, aloof he lived, until to dare
His dormant passions, Venus gave him fair
And lovely Galatea, lifelike grown,
But statue still. And then when he had known
Desire, the statue lived, his love to share.

Indeed, a care to the divine are those
Aspiring to unblemished good. Yet he
Who feels an honest human want elates
The gods. And Aphrodite knew, and knows,
A man, though unimpassioned he may be,
Must love an image he himself creates.

THE DEFENSELESS Connie Kledaras

Sometimes I am afraid. I lie
And shiver as the night boes by,
Thinking of the cold and weary world,
Of all the terror life can hold.

Shall my life's bestowment be
Of great value and fruit it bear?
Or shall my life's bestowment be
Of no value and despair?

As I lie awake at night
Thinking of my destiny
I ask my Lord who is my shepherd
To bestow on me His precious blessing.

So why should I, one strong and free,
Be frightened of my destiny?
Shall I not trust Omnipotence,
That shields and shelters innocence?

HALLOWEEN   Barbara Byrne

Witches and goblins and Hallowe'en frights -
Better not venture out this night of nights.
Broomsticks seem restless and eager to prance -
Even the trees move in queer, rhythmic dance.

Black cats and white sheets are prowling about -
Ghouls are the only things glad to be out.
Horrors keep honest folk frozen with fear --
My, but they're happy it's just once a year.

MY SEARCH   Diane Lizzadro

I looked, the night was dark and still,
And little did I see;
I looked, but naught came into view,
But yet, that strange voice called to me;
I spoke with question in my voice,
"Who calls from out this sea --
This sea of blackest hue,
Where that haunting voice won't let me be?"
I cried and begged to show to me
That voice, alone, that would set me free -
That voice, I found, was only He
Calling me to eternity.

POWER OF MUSIC   Bill Williamson

Music, sweet lilting music floats lightly
Over unsuspecting souls.
Filling their hearts with love and angelic
Beauty.

Light, airy music which makes their
Hearts gay and causes them to smile.
Music that makes their worries and cares
Seem far distant.

Music which opens a new and mystic world
By the magic power of rhythm and tone.
Music which handles them tenderly and
Lets them float on its light, airy melody.

SUNSET DREAM   Steven Hansen

When the sunset flames in the evening sky,
I'll always believe that my lover comes nigh.
She lives to the west where the fireball dips,
The red in the sky is the red of her lips.
The glow in the sky o'er the sungod's lair,
Is the glow of the light on my true love's hair.
On her finger she wears my ring of gold,
In the heavens it glitters a thousand fold.
The blue that surrounds the reddening glow
Reminds me of her, and a time long ago
When I held her close and saw in her eyes
A soft light there that now brightens the skies.

THE MIRROR   Teresa Benavidez

The mirror throws back its reflection
That is but a re-assurance of the truth
It mirrors back the bad or good intention
Of all deeds running rough or smooth
It gives the picture of reality
That we're all afraid to face
But stop and think it over quietly
And this source of truth embrace.

FREE!   Mary Hagen

It takes but a moment to pick a flower -
To see it wither and die;
But surely, 'tis better that God's little flower
Should stay and smile at the sky.

A beautiful bird in a golden cage
Would no doubt please the eye;
Yet surely, 'tis better to please the heart
And see the bird fly on high.

The babbling brook quite cheerily
Seems now and then to sigh:
"'Tis wonderful to know all things
Are just as free as I."

The glories of nature God made free;
And always should you and I
Thank Him for this and thank Him too
That we're free to smile at the sky!

WIND   Marion Smith

Oh wind that blows away
The grimy dust from the world;
That blows away the sweat and smell
From the city after the sticky sun
Has beat upon it the whole day.
That blows and breathes its cool, sweet breath
Upon the parched countryside in the summer
And takes away all ugly things;
It soothes my heavy heart as well.

RELEASED   Sara Ann Blackman

I've never known such happiness,
   Nor felt like Youth before -
The feelings that I've seen and read
   Now make my spirits soar!

Each day is treasured, to be lived -
   I feel so r i g h t,   so gay, so young!
My heart bursts from exuberance
   With joyful songs that m u s t be sung!

THE GOOD OLD DAYS   Mary N. Elder

My mother was a flapper;
   My daddy was a shiek.
And in the roaring twenties
   They reached their highest peak.

Daddy's pants were bell-bottom
      baggy,
Mother's hair was wind-blown
      shaggy.

Flagpole sitting was the
   current craze,
In what they called the
   good old days.

So let's drink a toast to
   the era they boast --
The godd old days.

REFLECTIONS   Ann Millington

As I walked in the dusk of the sweet eventide,
My thoughts were misty with dreams
Of summer days when breezes sighed
And flowers blossomed by streams.

When by night earth was cloaked in
                    a black velvet robe,
Which enfolded things near and far;
And high above our majestic globe
It was pinned by a silver star.

And trees were clothed in all shades of green;
Lakes were crystal clear;
Birds sang songs so sweet and serene,
And animals wandered near.

But, like all things, the summer dies,
The days turn crisp and cool;
And we are left with dreams and sighs;
Reflections in a pool.

YOUTH   Gale Simpson

What is this thing, youth? Here I shall tell you.
Youth is a spring bud filled with loveliness
Ready to burst forth with vigor so new,
Having success as its aim - nothing less.
Youth is a candle waiting to be lit;
Forever remaining a crystal light
So ready to work but never to quit,
To flame till the end of any fight.
Youth's a flicker of hope for the future
Whose radiant beauty leaves none to guess
That it looks to God for all its nurture
And its only secret is happiness.
Youth's the axis on which the world goes 'round,
But the essence of youth's yet to be found.

HAPPINESS   Mary Sue Shipe

Oh, what is happiness to you?
The outward, showy things of life,
Or inward joys no one can see?
For if it means those outward things,
The things that all the world can see
I fear that you have really missed
Your chance for real, true happiness.

ODE TO A CAMERA   Jane Schaefer

You sit on a shelf
    And wait to be used.
And when you are, you add another
    To the list of places you've cruised.

Winter, summer -
    All of the seasons
Folks doing things
    For uncanny reasons.
A newborn child
    On the threshold of life,
A wrinkled old man
    Who's faced all the strife.
Scenes that you smile on
    And those you abhor.
The happiness of peace-times,
    The wretchedness of war.
The folks who hold hate in their hearts
    And the others with love;
The sweet simplicity of those
    Who have faith in the great God above.

These are all scenes of the great panorama
That's passed through the eye of you, little camera.

WAVES   Jane Hohn

Ripples, growing into manhood,
Threatening, thunderous foam,
Spuring out from the breaks;
Rolling on forever,
Never tiring -
The Poet's love,
The Artist's dream.

MORTALITY   Jeanette Hosea

The wind was monstrous in its flight;
It tore and uprooted the old trees
Weakened by their duel with time.

When Spring arrived, she saw
No old ones to outline
With lovely leaves and budding branches;
She only glimpsed their long-dead bodies,
Lifeless on the ground.

WATER   James Long

Faucet water serves the elites,
        Faucet water serves the kings,
But the best that I can think of,
        Is the farmers' in the springs.

For water comes from faucets,
        But to get it work it brings,
While good clear mountain waters
        Rise unhindered in the springs.

HUMANITY VERSUS NATURE   Elizabeth Alexander

Down at the shore where the sea rolls in
And splashes a thundering, roaring din,
The air lis light with a damp salt spray
And seaweed's tangled sprawled array.
The wind sweeps by the barren dune
And the breeze in the weeds hums a rustling tune.
Driftwood's scattered bare and lone
Dried and bleached like forsaken bone.
Sandpipers skate across the scene
And Nature presides over all serene.
Callous it would be to intrude
On such impassing solitude.

To mar the view is the mark of man -
Bottles, orange peel, and a rusting can.

THE REASON   Edna Hobson

When the Holy Family
        Into Egypt made their flight,
At a poor old lady's dwelling
        They stopped to eat a bite.
And from a battered dipper
        She bade them take a drink
And when they had finished
        An angel came, I think!
And when they left, the lady looked
        But the dipper was not in sight
God rewarded all her kindness,
        Now it's in the stars at night!

WAR   Dorothy A. Goodwin

Why fight with swords or guns? Why not with tongues? -
'Tho' I myself were better at the first,
I always should consider it the worst:
Terror, hate, misjudgment are its wrongs,
And time inevitably brings about
Another war "to end all wars." And then -
After more calculation, and more men -
We enter "peace" - until they shout
That we have been attacked! The nation sits
Again to puzzle over its mistakes
And try to find out what it really takes
To beat this foe, forever call it quits.

It takes more brainwork, patience - not more wrath,
But we shall always take the easy path!

LIFE AND DEATH   Rita Kenyon

The candle of life
Melts beneath the flame of time
And grows slowly shorter
As the flame burns on.
At last the flame goes out
As the last piece of candle
Melts away.

NO!   Marjorie Hamann

My pen is poised high in the air,
The paper lies empty and white.
At wordless blue lines now I stare.
I shan't write a poem tonight!

I'll call her a Simon Legree.
Though others may shrink back in fright
She'll not make a slave out of me
I won't write a poem tonight!

I guess she must think that we're smart
And her bark isn't worse than her bite.
And I know she is cruel at heart
But I won't write a poem tonight!

For poetry I have no time
And it's almost a-quarter-to-three;
I can't think of words that will rhyme
So she won't get a poem from me.

140

CHALLENGE TO YOUTH   James Carlson

I speak for Democracy.
Democracy, with its ever-shining light,
Blazing the trail to freedom, justice, and righteousness
The very essence of our being, locked within that one symbolism
Creating government of the people, by the people, and for the people.
But without Democracy there is no freedom, justice, or righteousness,
And without Democracy there is no America;
Therefore, this heritage that we Americans take for granted
Cannot and must not stand alone.
For guidance . . . it turns to me
And I am youth.

TOMORROW'S DAY   Janet Jameson

Today the sky is blue and white;
Smoke from some deific pipe,
A sea of dreams, of love, of light -
Cool and clean a perfect type.

Tonight it will be dank and bare;
One huge dark and gaping space.
A star could never twinkle there;
Thunder and lighting claim his place.

But dream, love, be merry and then --
Tomorrow's day shall come again.

NIGHT RAIN   Joyce Krueger

Above, the moon sails in her kingdom of darkness,
Slowly she finds a pathway to a dark and lonely
                              lake,
And there gives to the earth her most magnificent
                              face.
Big and strangely white in the heaven, so she is
                      reflected in the water below.
A soft breeze stirs the water and the glow is
                shattered into a million silver lights.
The clouds begin to thicken and so sadly the moon
                kisses the water farewell.

The trees along the bank sigh and lift their
                green leaves to the soft, sweet rain.

BROTHERS WE   Shirley Anne Bauer

You're my brother - yes, you are,
    Black or White - from near or far.
My tongue - you may not understand,
    But this you will - to shake my hand.
My kind of work seems queer to you
    It matters not - for yours does, too.
We live so differently - you say,
    That-s right - but there - it's just our way.
You do the best that you can do?
    That's all that matters - I do too!
Financially - we differ - yes
    And socially - I must confess
Do we not strive for the same thing?
    And hope our lives some blessings bring?
We say we're different - oh - why bother
    We're all His sons - and He - our Father!

THE STARS   Verna L. Gill

The stars are eyes -
Eyes that watch the blackened earth,
Eyes that laugh at the stupid mistakes of mortals,
Eyes that have watched man since time began
        and will watch him 'til it ends.

THE FADED DOLL   Susan Schwarzkopf

I was but six
And I had a doll,
A rosy cheeked, golden tressed baby.
Her skin was soft -
Her blue eyes shone -
Her likeness to a real child
Was a wonder to me.
She was mine to love and cherish always.

Today I look once more
Upon my doll -
But my childhood has passed -
Her cheeks are faded,
Her blue eyes dead,
And her golden tresses, stringy -
Her likeness to a child has disappeared.
... Could I have really loved this
          lifeless rubber toy?

MUSIC   Nancy Gross

Merely a pleasant harmony of tone?
A blend of string and woodwind, these alone?
I SAW the spring in Norway: the fjord, the green, the sun!
I FELT the parting lovers' breaking hearts, the father's grief
                    and woe!
Within my heart the urgent hoofbeats echoed;
Before my eyes arose the Russian slave.
        I heard ---- but more;
        I felt, I saw ---- still more:
            I lived
            MUSIC.

THE BLACK APPLE   Nancy Lenz

Sun's sho shinin' bright this morn,
Makes a black boy glad he's born,
Them's red apples on that stand,
Not hard to get one, with my hand.

Whew! thank Ya Lawd, we's past that place,
Didn't take no apple, not a taste,
Ya devil, sho has handsome bait,
But Lawd, ah wants them pearly gates!!

EPITOME OF DAY   Leah Seeley

A semblance of dawn,
        alert in awakening,
Spreads welcomed light
        to raven corners.
Filled with expectancy,
        glowing with vigor,
Stirs and accepts all,
        equally offered.

Regal to give,
        a joy to possess,
Climaxing the height
        of heaven's ability.
Spreading peace to all,
        confined in its keeping,
Calmly it passes,
        to complete its tranquility.

DEATH   Joan D. Kilian

Death is like the leaves that fall unto the ground
   So soft, and quiet; yet, so sure.
That no one can tell what the hour
   Death shall knock upon your door.
And when it comes - Oh, be prepared
   Do heed my warning well.
Go out and lay the welcome mat, for
   Death rarely rings the bell.

ROME   Stephen Taylor

Oh, Rome, your seven hills you once did rule,
   And spread your empire fully 'round your world.
Your vaunted legions, merciless and cruel,
   Both far and near, your sparkling banners furled.

With power, wealth, and luxury of life,
   Your evils were your might, or so you thought;
And even when besieged in some great strife,
   Your enemies with jewels and gold you bought.

But were you truly beaten by the hordes,
   By myriad hosts of Germany and Gaul?
Nay, lofty city with your noble lords,
   By their own evils mighty empires fall.

So too, all powers which on sin now stand,
   Shall also crumble by God's mighty hand.

THE PATTERN OF THE UNIVERSE   Marcia Fullmer

   I saw a comet racing by
   Flinging flashes through the sky.
   With reckless glint it lit the night,
   Then fell to earth with no more light.

   Unlike the stars content to glow
   It had to make a flashy show.
   It used its power with one stroke,
   Then sailed to other spheres remote.

   The pattern of the universe
   Is in the heavens as on earth.
   Some flash their brilliancy and fall,
   While others shine to guide us all.

144

THE STRANGER — Ann Wallace

He marches as an army across a withered field
And strikes with all his terror 'gainst helpless sword and shield.
He obliterates the peasantry and those of noble birth --
Singling out his victims and crushing them to earth.

Sometimes he creeps mutely through stillness in the night,
Leaves with triumph glowing - victorious in his might.
He never hints his moving nor heralds his approach -
Stands silent in his conquest, far above reproach.

Yet this old withered creature uses not his scythe for crime.
He escapes the sight of mortals - never seen is Father Time.

IF WE BUT KNEW — Marianna Pieck

No one knows, but one can dwell
Yet even so, it's true we shall
Never know what would have been;
If we had done what we didn't do.

Our past, our present, our future, too,
Would be simpler; if we but knew
Why and when we ought to do
The things we should or should not do.

WHEN THE SNOW CAME DOWN
Charlotte Brown

When the snow came down, it came quietly.

When the rain came, it fell with the
Sound of bells.

When the wind came, it blew with the
Blast of trumpets.

When the sun came, it shone with the
Music of flues.

But when the snow came, it came with the
Whispers of sleepy children.

When the snow came down, it came quietly.

LIFE AND DEATH   James F. Hastings

What is death that we must fear
  The grave, so cold and grey?
'Tis but the night of rest before
  The everlasting day.

What is life but just a trial
  For what is yet to be?
So live thy life that when death comes,
  Thy God will honor thee.

BROTHERHOOD   Dianne Baumann

The Lord is Father to us all
  No matter what our race.
He cares not where we're from, nor what
  The color of our face.
He teaches us to love all men,
  No matter what their creed;
To always lend a helping hand
  When someone is in need.
So whether we're at work or play,
  On others let's not trod.
When we are tempted, let's recall
  We're all the sons of God.

REVERIES   Georgia Lee Travis

When the summer sun is shining
  a brilliant, flashing gold,
When to me it looks but dull,
  then I shall be old.

When I fail to see the beauty
  of autumn leaves turned red and gold,
When to me they are just leaves,
  then I shall be old.

When winter comes with its cloud-soft snow
  to cover my small fold,
When to me it is only snow,
  then I shall be old.

When spring with all its glory
  comes to brighten what we hold,
When to me it is but another season,
  then I shall be old.

IMMORTALITY   Jeanne Pond

Immortality of the soul
Forever seeking its revenge
Upon the hapless body of the unalike,
Who stands alone and unaware
Of when or where this tragedy may strike.
What fool! That knows not what the loss may be
Forbear - admit this Immortality.

REFUGEES   Judy Hirschhorn

Cold, hungry, weary, weary,
They move slowly down their lonely road,
Swaying, stumbling, crying, moaning,
Destination, only God knows.

Homes, families, peace, contentment,
All gone, perhaps never to return,
Homeless, sick, forsaken, desolate,
Their fate - A troubled world's concern.

Cruelty, oppression, slavery,
Lies heavy, hidden deep within their breasts,
Freedom, equality, justice,
In these only their salvation rests.

PEACE   Mary Holmes

Peace
Is a cold wind
Blowing around the corner of a barn.
Peace is a sky -
After sunset -
When the clouds have lost their glow
And cover the earth with blackness;
Peace is the sky
With its clouds
And its depth.
Peace is a farm:
The fields,
The woods,
The pasture.
Green alfalfa, golden wheat and oats -
In the dimness turned tan.
Peace
Is living with God.

FAME   Carolyn Dunkin

Only a true and honest name
Is ever needed to gain fame.
        Tho, fame to you may be
        Not all it seems to me.

To me it always seems that fame
Is something we must never claim.
        But always hold its key
        For other men to see.

OUR TREASURES   Peggy Vaughn

        The things recalled of days long past and gone
        Have stirred the pens of poets young and old:
        The mother's way of giving warmth to song;
        Her words, more treasured than a wealth of gold;
        The friendly dog you played with as a lad;
        The first few tearful days you spent at school;
        Long hours of toil and working with your dad;
        The days you stayed down at the swimming pool.
        By poet's pens and words of friends we learn
        The things that make this earth a worth-while place.
        And knowing these should make our hearts all yearn
        To pass them on that someone else might face,
        With higher hopes and greater peace of mind
        Because a friend has helped him these to find.

                AUTUMN'S TREASURE   Mary Jane Roman

        Autumn has a golden treasure,
        Seen in every countless leaf;
        Riches that no rule can measure,
        Nor a heart or mind conceive.

        Autumn has a matchless splendor,
        Pictured in its sapphire sky,
        Strewn with fleecy clouds that render
        Peace and beauty to the eye.

        Then as velvet folds of night
        Cast their richness o'er the earth,
        Shining, silvery points of light
        End the day in twinkling mirth.

CARNIVAL   Madelon Sommer

I see bizarre masks,
Paper mache,
And men drinking wine from golden flasks.
There's the gaudy song
Hollow in my ears
But resounding for the triumphant throng;
It's the world's fete!

MORNING SPLENDOR   Betty Lou Bresett

The breezes dance with flower and tree
The river rushes playfully free.

The hills begin to stretch and yawn
As if to say, "Wake up, it's dawn."

The dewdrops lay their sleepy heads
Upon the grass they've used for beds.

The dainty foot-prints of the deer
Clearly show that they've been here.

Mother Nature extends her hand
And welcomes all to see her land.

MELODY   Catherine King

The moods of song are strange indeed,
On lilting waves of sound they go,
To carry there like a flashing steed
Their strains of love and joy and woe.

A dreamy tune that speaks of love,
Will tell a heart that's sad and small
Of Goodness coming from above,
And mortal love, if that's our call.

A lively song much joy can yield,
In strange, but bright and happy ways,
That spirit found in lowly field
Will rise into a higher phase.

But still in melody we find
A sense of woe as yet untold,
These things we see so clear in mind,
Begin with music to unfold.

FOG   Kaye Raymond

The fog rolls in o'er land and sea,
And cools the brow of the likes of me,
The lamps on the street seem to flicker and die
Just to rise up again as a breeze passes by,
The houses I see look like ghosts in the dark,
A tossed-away match casts a flickering spark,
It covers the town like a great gray shroud
And settles to rest, so haughty and proud.
All through the night it watches o'er all,
The clouds of it rise, and whisper, and fall
And then, having stayed from the eve till the dawn,
The fog lifts its armor and moves on, and on.

FANTASY   Billie Vancel

I danced with the wind one balmy night
On a rocky summer shore
And very much to my delight
The wind danced with me, o'er and o'er
The clouds rose high and tip-toed by
So not to break the spell
The gulls flew past and winked an eye
My secret not to tell
The waves leaped up to wash the shore
The traces of me gone.
The wind ceased, I danced no more
For now has come the dawn.

DEATH   Maryellen Fullam

I heard his footsteps faintly in the night
Like waves that fall upon a distant shore
And being young and gay and fleet of foot
I quickly fled and left him far behind.

In middle life the echo louder came
Like muffled tom-toms in the jungle gloom
And being strong and filled with zest for life
I turned my back and filled my cup again.

But now the setting sun grows dim and fades
My limbs are stiff, I can no farther go
I hear his footsteps nearer to me draw
I cannot flee, I sink and cannot rise.

TO THE ARTS   Virgilia Z. Heimsath

Whene'er I hear the vibrant keys of Liszt
And languish in the greatness of his art,
Or thrill to Rembrandt's brush so heavenly kiss'd
I stop, and ecstasy enthralls my heart.

To art! to those whose gifts will bring the light
When darkness seems to brood on spirits free!
To those whose hymns and prayers will vanquish fright,
'Till once again our eyes are made to see.

To those who praise the muse and love as I
The Arts so cultivated everywhere,
The symphonies whose strains attain the sky,
And nestle in the West Wind's swirling air.

To Art! a light in gloom, we offer praise;
The core of life, to you our hymns we raise.

SYMPHONY   Diane Van Winkle

To me, a rose is a symphony
With tones like those of a harp;
Its petals soft, yet clearly defined,
Its odor, sweet and sharp.
Its bud, so like an overture,
A building of the theme;
The finale, bursting in full bloom,
A symphony supreme.

WHEN GENTIANS LAST IN THE CLASSROOM
BLOOMED   Norma Migdoll

He brought them in the classroom bare,
Sweet gentians found in number rare,
He brought them in 'mid his despair
When they smiled not in rapture fair.

They grew far paler than the moon,
The students' handling was no boon;
They grew far paler as their doom
With darkened face did near them loom.

They drooped in death away from land
Of gentian field with gentian band;
They drooped in death, and now they stand
More beauty killed by human hand.

A WALK AND A THOUGHT   Leona Pettit

While I was walking in the woods one day,
Down a grass-grown path I chanced to stray;
And there amidst the shrouded pines
There was no thought of war - no signs.

Blessed with this peace, I wondered why
We've such a troubled world, you and I?
Why brother fights brother, and death is the score?
Why nature's so rich - humanity so poor?

A PLEDGE TO DEMOCRACY   Evan Jay Spelfogel

Land of freedom and democracy,
Utopia of freeman's dreams,
Dwelling place of the poor and the needy,
Home of those with means,
To you I pledge my allegiance.

Land of freedom and democracy,
Sanctuary of law and justice,
Domain of peace and tranquility,
Realm of independence,
To you I pledge my allegiance.

THE SHELL   Sandys Moore

The shell that crispy 'round a turn
so dulls the blade's edge to a quiet,
has beauty more than none should tell
but only that which rocks it slowly
and chides it by the foam of waves.
It gently holds the sound of seas,
of salty wynde, of rustic cry
from a chance bird on flight towards sun.
The glance of light from dying sky
transforms the slight and careful shell
into a perfect thought of pink.

The breaking waves wash pure the skeleton,
yet ever hold the closeness of its beauty.
Majesty lies scarcely high toward sun,
and sound is held by the eternity.

SPRING'S LOOSE IN TOWN Irmgard Wacker

Ocean Parkway's gilded by the sun;
Fifth Avenue's bright with chic chapeaux de France.
The vernal equinox has winter on
The run; there's gaiety in every glance.

Forsythia's bright on Riverside Drive;
The Botany class takes to the field.
Durocher clamors; the rookies strive.
Young love with kisses is happily sealed.

There's painting of boats on City Island sand;
In Rockefeller Plaza tulips bloom,
The cardboard goat announces his bock beer brand.
The Palmolive bride smiles at the Kre-mel groom.

The rash of clover in Central Park's a sight;
There's smell of earth and life! This Spring's all right!

THE DEVASTATING STORM   Joy Van Wye

The wind-swept fields, once again,
Were struck with the hidden force of rain;
The sky grew dark, the lightning flashed,
The trees bent low as thunder crashed.

The water deep in gullies lay
Eroding the earth and tearing away;
The trees so beautiful in the fall,
Now stand leafelss, gaunt, and tall.

ON BECOMING HAPPY WHILE WRITING A SAD
POEM Shirley Ann Nord

My fleeting inspirations
Have come, and now have fled;
The body of my poem
Was wounded and is dead.

I'll bury it with sorrow
And choose another task;
My lingering emotion
With cheerful face I mask.

Goodbye, my little poem,
You served your purpose, true;
But happiness o'ertook me
And was the death of you.

NIGHT OVER THE PARK   Rae Huffstutler

At eventide, I used to wander, not too long ago,
To see the beauty of a park, to watch the river flow.
The birds would pass me overhead, wheeling left and right;
Then quickly swoop and sim and dive, before resuming flight.
A rising wind deranged each tree, lifting its boughs on high;
Reminding one of mighty arms, reaching toward the sky.
The heavens flamed, shadows lengthened, the river raced, grew dark;
The sun sank down behind the hills, and night fell o'er the park.

CALIFORNIA   Eleonore Stansell

California! Land of blazing sunsets and glowing sunrises;
Land of ancient ruins where Indians used to roam;
Land of astonishing histories full of surprises.
Glorious California - my home.

California; where old haciendas still stand
While ghostly senoritas and caballeros gaily dance.
California; where past and future are bound by the hands
Of predestination and chance.

California, home of movies and missions,
Land of starry skies seen through the observatory's dome.
Golden land where dreamers vision
The future. California - my home.

THE GOLDEN YEARS   Ronald Wilcox

O, Memory, speed not away
On the jealous wings of time,
But linger on awhile, and stay,
Thou storyteller sublime.

Tell me of years gone by,
When we laughed, sang, and misbehaved,
Remind this weary mind of why
Those moments are not lost, but saved.

Let me gaze once more upon
Familiar faces, joy, and tears,
For they're with me still, never gone.
Yes Those were the Golden Years.

CHANGED IDEAS   Stanley Carpenter

When we are small we wish to be tall,
Tall as the tallest of men.
We pray for that day and hope for that day
When we'll be as big as our kin.

But when that day comes, it comes to us all,
We recall those grand days with a grin.
As we go to and fro with our duties and woe,
We wish we were kids again.

MY LIKES   David Wells

I like the scent of pine and sage,
Of wind from a field of new mown hay,
The sight of moonlight bright as day,
The sound of coyotes far away.

I like the smell of food that we cook,
The sound of water running in the brook,
I lie there listening to the sounds so sweet,
The sounds of the wilderness at my feet.

I like the smell of spring in the air,
The sight of plants blooming everywhere,
The sound of voices free from care,
The laughs of a couple over joys that they share.

SONNET I   Margo Archibald

A feeling of woe enclosed my heart
As I wandered along life's weary way;
The day seemed dreary, the day seemed dark -
How lonely can a person stay?
I had not a friend to comfort me
In this solitude of grim despair;
My thoughts were empty, my feelings low,
For I had no one who could care.
But then the day dawned bright for me -
A feeling warm engulfed my soul
And spread throughout my aching heart.
I saw your face with laughing eyes -
Your smile entranced me like a gem
And life within me flowed again.

DIFFERENCES IN SIZE   Marjorie Gleicher

I walk along and see the many trees
So regal when they stand or start to sway.
And on the boulevard there is a breeze,
Which you would feel if you should walk my way.
Flowers line my path each day I walk;
The air is fresh and lovely is the sky;
The people friendly when I stop to talk.
As in the morning I am passing by.

But, oh, so different are the city ways;
The rushing of the people on the street
And traffic passing leave me in a daze;
So strange are these, the people that I meet.
The life that seems to me to be unwise
Is just the country with a greater size.

GOD'S PURPLE   Nancy Beardsley Stiles

The heavens opened
      and the rains came.
The sun cast its rays
      upon the frosted earth.
A gentle violet inched
      its way from russet warmth,
Uncurled its pale green leaves,
      and trusted its frailty to God.

TO CHOPIN THE POET   Cindy Jones

"Chopin the poet has long been dust -
In life he never was robust ... "
    And yet your works on wings still fly
    Throughout the world and still belie
The changing times. Your fate was just!

Yours was a soult that felt it must
Let loose to man your heart, your gust
    Of smiling tears, both brave and shy,
        Chopin the poet

You put your hopes, your fears, your lust
For gems of music all in trust
    To jealous men. Yet do not sigh,
    Your work still lives. You cannot die
Until the world's forever hushed,
        Chopin the poet.

PROOF?   Pat Ambrose

The diamond jewel of morning dew
As it rests on the velvet rose,
The soft sighing of a summer breeze,
The graceful dip of a swallow's flight,
The lap of the waves as they caress
The faces of the rocks,
The graceful walts of the clouds
As they glide across the stage of blue --
Yet there are those who doubt
             His existence.

RE-BIRTH   Lois Swearinger

A gaunt and blackened tree leans by my house . . .
             Today the sunlight wove a
             Mist of golden shadows 'round its barrenness
             As though to keep from it the
             Aching cold of winter's frosty breath.
             Last night a troop of leering wind-ghosts
             Crept through its creaking limbs,
             Their bloodless shrieks resounding
             Through the starless night.
             Their dragging chains of ice
             Bit through the outer shell of bark and
                        Green showed through.

A gaunt and blackened tree leans by my house . . .
        But Time is good,
           And Spring will come again.

A STROLL ON THE BEACH   Dorothy Boleman

I love to walk upon the silvered sands,
To feel the beat of waves upon the shore,
To hold the pearly shells within my hands,
And listen to the surfhead's sounding roar.
I love to watch the seagulls as they sweep
Down to the beach, on silent feathered wing,
To seize a prize, a tidbit from the deep,
Or dine on that the sea may wish to fling.
I love to feel the coolness of the breeze
That sweeps from 'cross the shores of froeign lands
To bring me dreams of sailing ships at sea,
And salty tales of men with sturdy hands.
Yes, this I love, the joy and gentle peace,
When strolling where the waves do never cease.

FAIR WISH   Peggy Hartle

Would I were the night that walketh
Through great marble halls,
With skirts of sable tiered with light
From wide and darkened walls.
I'd blanket hearts to sorrow bound,
With velvet touch, and calm
The wearied mind, and heal the soul
With soft and cooling balm.

A WINTER NIGHT   Jacqueline Ameling

O wintry night with starlit gleam,
I love thy solitude,
Like blanket o'er the world asleep
You cast your tranquil mood.

O wintry night with mystic moonlight
Beaming on the glistening snow,
While whimpering wintry breezes
Toss pine trees to and fro.

O wintry night, while thou dost reign
O'er snowy fields all dazzling bright,
Strolling 'neath thy velvet skies
Is truly sheer delight.

STATUS QUO   Carol Mahlke

Each snowflake
Gently taking its place
To make a blanket of white feathers
Has a purpose to fulfill.
Each star
Daintily taking its place
To form a pattern of murals
Across the sky
Has a purpose to fulfill.
Each blade of grass
Gracefully taking its place
Among the rest in a sea of green
Has a purpose to fulfill.

So also every human being
Takes his place in life
While fate decides
What purpose he'll fulfill.

BLEAKNESS   Susan Weiner

A steel-gray sky, streets lined with barren trees -
Industry's piercing shriek announcing five -
Workers await their buses to return
To one-room flats of crumbling cold, gray stone -
A starving cat, a once plump feline beauty,
Now shows projecting ribs and mangy fur,
Matted fur made gray by soot and filth -
Yes, frigid gray enveloping all in sight
Awaits in death-like still to claim the next.

THEY ALSO SERVE WHO WAIT   Lou Raw

The crisis carries him away so far,
From out of realism into a dream.
The parting moments strangely unreal seem;
Farewell in nature's picture is a scar.
So "Bon voyage" whispers my heart with pain;
"May God protect you," say my eyes through tears.
Until we meet again though it seem years
Our memories enchanted will remain.
All happiness can fall to emptiness,
And sorrow's hours replace those hours of joy.
But let not worry now your mind annoy,
Nor let a loss give life one meaning less.
Let striving for success be paradise.
My memory then will be sweet sacrifice.

JEWELS   Donna Linfoot

Sapphire, the sky over head,
Lacy the tree arms outstretched:
Emerald, the carpet of grass,
Velvet to touch at each step.
Topaz, the primrose in bloom,
Huddling in clusters together;
Pearl-white narcissus so graceful,
Greeting new blossoms each morn.
Garnet and full every tulip
Happily nodding their heads;
Diamonds in dew drops that sparkle;
Reflecting the coming of dawn.

Priceless our jewels in the garden,
To welcome us early in spring.

BROTHERS   Moonyean Szofran

Dirty cherubic faces,
Smiling when happy,
Tear-stained when sad.
Mischievous little creatures,
Especially at the age of
Not quite five,
And a little past seven.

I MUST REMEMBER   Beverly Jean MacInnis

I must remember to forget
A moonlit river tide,
The sound of waves that fringed its bank
You, whispering by my side.

I must remember to forget
Clear, cool-cut evenings in September,
The song of rain, the warmth of spring,
Instead, I must remember -

That laughter if it's gay enough
Can dull the sound of dying,
That hearts weren't made to wear outside,
And tears are not for crying.

BLACKBOARDS   Juliana Hughes

Can anyone measure the knowledge
That a blackboard must contain,
All sorts and kinds of wisdom
Born in someone's brain?

If it could only walk and think
And speak as we are able,
We all could learn such wondrous news
Not told in books or fables.

All through the year he never moves,
Like lonely sentinel he stands;
But Father Time must take his toll,
And make him prey to cruel demands.

He's stood at top of rooms and seen
The dreams of children long ago;
And he will see in future years
The things our children know.

SNOW   Keith Mills

To thee, O Snow, an ode we owe;
      Thy glistens make sparkles where dirt used to show.
Each feathery flake above the earth hovers,
      Then plummets downward and a piece of earth covers
In its shimmering whiteness.

Each flake while resting side by side,
      Forms mountains, and waves like the incoming tide
Frozen and flaked on its way to the shore,
      Only to melt and flow once more
In its trickling lightness.

ALTER IDEM   Judy Allen

The hour was dead when the clock struck,
The hour before had been the pursuer
And had done his job so very successfully.
And now, when the clock struck again,
There was not just one dead hour,
But heaps and heaps of colorless minutes
Waiting for me to venture into them --

Motionless minutes that meant that
I was me and all that was mine was part
Of myself. My tangled spider-webbed self.

THE AUTUMN HAZE   Wilma Spainhour

Some call it Indian campfires
When the haze enfolds the country.
Deep it stands in the valleys,
Drifting like a lost soul
Coming and going on silken feet.
Walking with ghostly hand on my shoulder,
Ever near yet just out of reach,
Leaving a dewy stillness,
Bringing a lonesome tone,
A veil,
  a mist,
    a spirit -
This mystic autumn haze.

WIND   Betty Rhodes

Wind is the ghost of winter,
The ghost that darts over the barren fields,
The ghost that dances with the autumn leaves,
'Till spring the air has filled.

FIGURE FROM THE PAST Marjorie Williams

A red skin blazed against the purple dusk
A dauntless courage shone as rays from deep
And cunning eyes, unflinching eyes that scanned
The vast expanse of golden plains,
Eyes which knew so well and loved a land
Of plenty, eyes so void of care,
Eyes a part of one proud frame that
Rode astride a great paint horse, a frame
That bore a yet unconquered heart
And radiated majesty!

LOST   Irene Barber

There comes the awakening,
Then the rebirth,
The love of beauty that is there
Of words, souls, and earth.

But stay, for within the day,
It will be broken,
As the waves that lash
Against the jagged edges of the coastline.

The waves continue endlessly,
But each and every one is destined
Only to be broken
And forgotten.

So it is with us, on and on until ....
We reach the coastline, the inevitable
Where dreams are broken and souls are torn,
Flung to the winds.

Lost in the churning and pounding,
Lost in the turbulence of an infinity,
Only to be recaptured as a memory,
And we must forever live in reality.

TO A SNOWFLAKE   Margie Anthony

When shadows fall at night with silv'ry blend,
I love to lie beside the fire and dream
Of snowflakes white and the brilliance they lend,
To change the drabness of "Old Winter's" scheme.
There are no two flakes alike in true design,
And as they spiral from the sky aloft
They form a blanket of unbroken line,
That turns the barren bleakness smooth and soft.
Like snowflakes, folks are diligently designed,
But that is all; the likeness there doth cease.
In warlike fury, nations stand aligned
And will not join together to form peace.
If men like flakes would mingle tranquilly,
'Twould blanket earth with blessed harmony.

THE WEEPING WILLOW TREE   Deirde Ditchfield

Down at the corner of our land,
A weeping willow tree does stand.
Symbol of our childhood dear,
I'll always hold its memory near!

It's the guardian of our hopes and dreams,
The throne-room of our kings and queens;
As 'neath its branches we have laid,
The things that we alone have made.

And fondly now it gathers us in,
Regardless of our kith and kin;
It shows us all the way back home
However far we may have roamed.

THE YARDSTICK   Joanne Whitney

O Spirit of the mountain lofty,
Can you tell the reason why,
Men, who on your peaks seem lowly,
In the valley seem so high?

O traveller on life's weary highway,
Dweller of the lowland sod,
The valley measures up from earth;
The mountain measures down from God.

COMMENT   Joan Vames

In the sun's rays
A bulb burns,
Unnoticed,
Losing its brilliance.

In infinite darkness
Radiant it shines,
Unflickering,
Flaunting its small fire.

ANNE BOLEYN   Joanne Zimmer

Sweet enchantress, did you think
To live out all your stolen years in peace?
How wrong you were, how cruel!
And yet, maybe you had no choice,
For Harry was a dashing love, and you were young.
And so you fought with all your charming witchery
And won a little time in which to laugh
And sing your songs before the end.
You died a gallant death, my Anne, and winning yet,
For immortality is yours, and Harry shan't forget.

TWILIGHT   Betty S. H. Burriss

The trees' firm, lofty branches upward wind
To touch the blue;
As man may seek, but seldom hope to find
A heart that's true.

While far above life's never ceasing tide
Fair fades the day;
In flaming golden hues that briefly bide
And then, away.

Draw nigh, yon pale shadows of the eve
And calm the dell.
What though the misty twilight oft' deceive
And cast its spell?

Yet evening fades, and twilight is a dream
Beheld afar;
While through the coming darkness, lo, is seen
One twink'ling star.

164

DAWN   Carol Kragh

A little moon slipped down the sky;
Behind it crept a cloud,
The winding wind came whimpering past
And breathed a sigh aloud.

A star slipped past me as I watched,
And silently went its way;
Then like the burst of a blossoming bud
There broke the light of day.

CONSOLATION   Carolyn McGlone

Consolation is sought in various form
To quiet the suffering some souls endure.
To the strings of music some souls forlorn
Cry out for justice; seek to conjure.
In a rage of anger and laughing scorn
Vengeance seek; but pity secure.
In the realms of nature seek to adorn
Their blackest thoughts; peace to procure.
Through a word from those a soul is born
Comes light in darkness; life's path allure.
Each soul is varied in means to conceive
Consolation which heals, nourishes and feeds.
In times of trying my soul too grieves
Consolation I've found in my rosary beads.

NOTHING LASTS   Shirley Jean McKelvey

All is finished, all is fought,
All is done, and all is wrought;
Now the gym stands dark and quiet
Though a game raged just tonight.
Cool night winds blow at my face . . . .
So the world is like this place.
Nothing lasts, yes, all things pass;
Even you, my little lass
In your gown and jewels fine
You, yes, you will fade with time.
Castles crumble, empires fall;
God's the victor over all.
Nothing of this world's secure,
Only things of God are sure.

WAR   Nelson James Dunford

Death's trumpet breaks the silence of the air
resounding in the vastness of unfathomed hell
as once again - always and always once again -
man slips the bonds that feign to hold
God's likeness to a God-like life.
Now, as before, the gore and blood of men
Is freely scattered on the land and left uncleaned
and yet man dares to speak of lasting peace
while hell sits chuckling by its open gates -
laughing at the worthlessness of such talk.

JUST FOR THE ASKING   Marcia Bell

I never asked for anything
but just to live and love.

I never prayed for anything
but guidance from above.

I never asked for anymore
nor anymore received.

And yet I've lived a richer life
than could ever be believed.

MEN WORK   Ralph Haworth

In the golden fields of wheat
Underneath the burning ball of fire
Men work . . .
Underneath the ground in the dark
Ebony-chambers in the cellars of the world
Men dig . . .
On sea washed decks that roll
And pitch keeping time with the waves
Men sweat . . .
On the blood-scarred battle grounds
Where sinners and saints pray together
Men die . . .
All over the world men work, men dig,
Men sweat, men die so that
Men may live . . .

MY PEACE   Jacquelyn Vaughan

In some dark hours I tread the road
Of hate, and sore contempt my load.
The way is hard, each step a curse,
Without God's love my soul doth thirst.
For by this way no love is found,
And all my hopes in tears are drowned.

From this path my shadow will fall
Upon my friends, my neighbors, all;
For Lo! the love of war with me
Does travel on and on, yet I cannot see.
Blind am I to good, and faithless too,
Peace cannot be with me, God, without you.

CHALK SOLDIERS   Virginia Thomas

Chalk soldiers march across the blackboard,
But I cannot see.
Staccato beats pound, pound on the slate,
But I cannot hear.
They form letters on the blackboard,
But I cannot read.
They break their ranks to move into words,
But I cannot understand.
                              Chalk soldiers!

O PEACE   Lois Linder

The nations cry out, O Peace,
And the echo comes back in gunfire
As war sounds round the world.

The peoples cry out, O Peace,
And they are mocked by the dead
Lying slaughtered in the field.

Oh, where is the Peace we cry for?
Oh, when is that Peace we die for?
And the answer comes back, "There is none,"
And the echo comes back, "There is none."

Yet, somewhere there must be Peace,
And sometime War must cease;
That place is in the heart of man
When hatred has lived its span;
For Peace is found only through love
And faith in our God above.

A NOCTURNE   Janice Rudin

Under the burning eyes of night,
There blooms a crimson-shaded rose -
A Nocturne -
Named for the perfect eves
It represents.
Beautiful ripples of red,
A flower of dreamy moods,
Fragrant as the starlit winds of night
And sweetly sentimental as the haunting strains
Of a half-remembered serenade.

THE PASSING SEASONS   Diana Messenger

Winter seeks the leaves
But she cannot bring forth.

Spring foresees the leaves
In the tender little bud.

Summer finds the leaves
In their fullest green.

Autumn frees the leaves
And lets them flutter down.

I SAW THE HILLS OF KOREA
Donna Anderson

I saw the hills of Korea, dark,
Stained with warriors' blood.
I heard the cannons boom and roar,
I saw men crawl in mud.
I heard them scream
I saw them die
I saw them writhe with pain,
I saw the skies grow dark above
And wondered where the blame.

I wonder in Korea, dark,
Is there no peace nearby?
Is there no God to stop this war,
To stop their painful cry?
To bring men peace,
To bring them hope,
To let them live again,
To bring them to their homes once more
To see the shining sun.

LONGING   Barbara Cohn

I want to feel the fresh, damp earth
          under my restless feet.
I want to dig my toes far into the
          nourishing earth,
          and lie deep in the sweet-smelling grass,
          surrounded by high trees,
          and a cool blue sky.
And if I should tire of this,
I would like to see
        the sea,
          thundering endlessly,
           stretching
            far.
        Of this I could not tire.

AWAKENING   Marie Rita Zafian

How softly words can lift a saddened heart
Reflect a shyness, yet unfurl a spark
Of poetic genius, a love of nature true,
No longer will this burdened heart be blue.
A poet's dream has lighted up my way,
His thoughts and joys in my heart forever stay.
What joys these verses bring to me;
Such ecstasy has set my sad heart free!

PATHS   Eugene Wright

I tramped a path in deepest snow
In many passings to and fro.
And lo, when I looked back to see,
A little child was following me.

Then dawned the lesson God had sent;
To me His message this had meant;
We tramp the paths through life's long flow
Which others follow as they go.

Beware, that where your travels lead
They follow paths worn down with heed
For sometimes, not so far away,
Someone may take the path you lay.

WORDS   Vera Dawes

Words that go for weeks unsaid
Are twice as painful as tears unshed.
They are kept down deeply rooted inside
And make you wish you could have cried.
They remain as a whisper, somewhere in view;
The phrases are simple with meaning quite true.
And yet your mouth closes - you simply can't tell
But if you were alone - you'd be able - quite well.

SONNET   Enid Smith

When the symbol of hope and faith in man
Is darkened by the shadow of evil,
The miracle we've sought since time began
Will ne'er appear to our blind eyes until
We realize this miracle is love,
And has forever been within our grasp.
'Tis not a thing that falls from up above
Nor springs from ground below for us to clasp.
To those who look beyond themselves for aid,
This miracle will be obscure as night.
To those who love, the gloom and fear will fade
And in its place, the blaze of sunshine bright
Will clear the skies with hope - renewed, unbound.
And we shall cry - "The miracle is found!"

TWILIGHT   June H. Vann

As softly as the summer breeze
   The light began to fade.
An unseen hand began to paint
   With colors deep as jade.

Then quietly as a falling leaf
   It stole across the sky.
The copper sun began to sink
   And died without a sigh.

As brightly as the sparkling dew
   The stars began to light
The velvet sky, so soft and pink,
   As twilight changed to night.

THE SOUNDS OF DEATH   Robert Gillooly

A sudden flash lights up the heavens with a blinding glow;
   A low, vibrant hum grows stronger;
  Men cringe in fearful anticipation
     Lives hang in the balance;
  The awed silence is broken by a shattering explosion.
  The air is filled now with a hushed, unnatural calm.
     Presently, other sounds follow:
    Shrill, pathetic groans of dying men -
These are the sounds of war and destruction;
  These are the sounds of death.

DESTINY   Ted Howes, Jr.

Life is unpredictable.
  A mission guided
By the Father infallible.
  This is Destiny.

Death is inevitable.
  The foreboding messenger
Of the Father ineffable.
  This is Destiny.

ONE WAY   Edna E. Solari

As I turn the pages of life
  I title my book, "One Way"
And in each chapter my tales of strife
  Are written there to stay.

My evil deeds are recorded in Black,
  My good deeds in Gold,
Which outweighs the other?
  Only God seems to know.

The climax of my treasured book
  Arrives when my goal is attained,
Then will I dare to look
  To see, what I have gained.

On judgment day the world will know
  Of my deeds recorded in Black and Gold,
Will I be shy to let others see
  What kind of a life was led by me?

CONCEIT   Daniel Salvante

It stands there pale in a darkening sky,
A thing of ages, of times gone by.
A question mark hung over the heads of men,
To make them go over their thoughts again.
Space speckled over ever so fine,
Takes us beyond the walls of time,
To when He Who created
Gave no thought to creation,
Of living tissue or breathing blood,
Of conceited ones to look up to the sky and think,
"Doubtless the stars were made for made for man."
Yet, the stars were there before man began.

PROPHECY   Marjorie Speece

This is the ageless prophecy, grave warning
Of the things to come; foreseen by none
Save only those who dreamed it in an hour
Of tribulation, or saw it in a night
Of fiendish glee:

Ruthless Pride has struck her mortal blow
And man lies wounded in the dust of Time,
A broken, cursing mass, leaning more toward
Death than Life; and waiting, always waiting
Until the Man of men shall come again
And bind the passive soul to its last destiny.

THE RIVER   Sheryl Stephen

Rushing, swirling, foaming,
The muddy river flows.
Churning past tall buildings,
Made of clay and wood and stone.

Roaring, spraying, tumbling,
Over sharp grey rocks it rolls,
Running past the farm lands,
Past the meadows brown and gold.

Rippling, gurgling, swishing,
Through shadowed lanes of trees,
Flowing ever onward,
Till it meets the cool, green seas.

SPRING ON WOLF RIVER   Charlotte Davis Dean

The water crept in like a pouting child -
Its sullen yellowness swelled over its banks
And hesitated, then rolled swiftly on
Into the green cornfields with such vigor
That all the crows cawed wildly, leaving corn
For the pale, murky, swift, mad flood.

ANY GIRL   Alfred Borgen

She's sugar and spice,
        She's strawberry ice;
She's moonlight and roses,
        And loaded dice;
Today she'll splurge,
        And tomorrow, skimp;
She's Carrie Nation,
        And Helen-of-Troy;
Elaine and Scarlet,
        And Myrna Loy;
She's real as trouble;
                Who???
Any girl at all since Eve!

OH, YOU DREAMER   Elnora Whitaker

Oh, you dreamy, dreaming dreamer.
Just think of what I say.
Oh, why are you so insistent?
    I can't write a poem!

Oh, the printers, painters, writers,
Oh, the singers, speakers, actors;
They were dreamers just like you, but
    I can't write a poem!

Oh, the many, many years
Oh, the dreamers in that time.
Oh, why will you just insist?
    I can't write a poem!

Oh, I dream of many things
To sing about, to talk about,
But no matter how I try
    I just can't write a poem!

FRIENDLY WIND   Ann Webster

The passing wind has always been a kindly friend to me,
Because in lonely moments, it has kept me company.
All along the streets where people pass without a word,
It has important messages, that only few have heard.
The messages of memory, that fill a friendly breeze,
When it is whispering softly among the swaying trees.
The wind has made me ready for the winter's icy hold,
By howling down the chimney place, to warn me of the cold.
Each spring it has invited me to leave my work and play.
And always it has tried so hard to blow my cares away.

SONGS   Rodney Prinz

Now, there are songs that are brought to life,
Like the wind and then the rain.
They spread their joy or leave their tears,
And then they're gone again.

There are those that make their bid
And are accepted by a few,
But soon they are forgotten
And settle like the dew.

Yes, there are the ones that soothe your heart,
Or make you want to cry;
And it seems there are some so very old,
They'll never, never die.

GOALS   Pat Formet

It has been said that those who try
Can gain the highest peak.
But what of him who has no goal?
What fortune shall he seek?

Or must he satisfy himself
Until his time shall end
With toiling on the foothill road
That never seems to bend?

The answer is not written here,
For we do not yet know
If goals are always mountain peaks
Or are the plains below!

THE MASTER PAINTER   Alice Price

The snow lay thick upon all the ground
As far as my eye did penetrate.
The wind swept on with a mournful sound
And left behind the brown trees desolate.

But then came spring with blossoms fair
And gay little birds of color bright
To sing and chirp and fill the clear warm air
With sweet music and beauty of rare delight.

Long summer days, bright sun, and azure sky,
Bright golden harvests of ripened grain,
Maples flaunting yellow and red on high,
Orchards laden with apples along the lane.

So dear old Mother Nature with paint brush in hand
Uses all her colors in the endless panorama of the land.

CONTRASTS   Carol Fray

In distant lands, like flocks of sheep astray,
Men wander o'er the barren, wasted, land
Lost, and like a spider spin a web
Of dank despair around their tortured souls.

And yet, far off, a field of corn and wheat,
Will swirl and sway beneath the noonday sun,
And men, with fervid hopes and dreams will live,
     Within a world of perfect solitude.

CITY SYMPHONY   Joan M. Filia

Silence walks with noiseless feet
Through every building, every street.
And then behind the walls of grey
Comes rosy Dawn, who brings the day.

The city stirs from quiet sleep,
As sunbeams through each window creep.
Its eager heart begins to beat,
As crowds of people fill the street.

The traffic sounds swell to a hum;
The city's symphony's begun.

TO AN OLD HOME   Ann Roller

I hate to see a lovely home grown old,
Neglected, empty, needing paint and care,
No longer tight against the rain and cold,

But windy, mouldy, hinting of damp air.
The lawn which once was velvet smooth and green
Is tangled like a stray dog's rough hair.

The kitchen which was once scrubbed bright and clean
Is home for mice; the dust in piles is deep,
And echoes sound where Sheraton has been.

I want no new-built modern house to keep;
I'd rather wake a huge old home from sleep.

THROUGH FIELDS   Sharon M. Long

The moon shines between tombstone stalks -
Silent sentinals to summer.
They mark the grave of used-to-be
And what can be no more . . . .

The winds rustle the rusty leaves -
Lifeless leaves scorched in summer sun -
Made brittle by chaffing winds
That wind their way through fields.

SPRING   Pat George

I caught a glimpse of spring today
    Donning her summer gown
And saw a blade of grass push through
    The thawing earth so brown.

I saw her break her frozen coat
    Of ice on a shallow lake
And saw her place a touch of color
    Upon a frosted cake.

I watched while all the birds returned
    And buds broke out on trees
And prayed to God to keep them there
    And never let them freeze

176

MEDITATION   Gene Carlock

When the peace comes, will I be here,
Or will I go to rest among the others
Who have already gone – seeking and
Not finding?

Can you tell me or do you know of what I speak?
Is it not a dream?
Or can it come to those who lie
In hope and wait?

There is one way, one path, one light
Which we must take
And never cease
To want.

SEA SYMPHONY   Harriet Fronk

I lay on a cliff, one windy day,
And listened to the sea.
A symphony of deepest sound
Was what it seemed to me.

And as I lay, the wind died down
The drums became a flute
A soothing gentle undertone
Of a cello, soft and mute.

TO A CRICKET   Viola Ryder

The cricket strums his lullaby;
He plucks his soporific song
Upon his fiddle. Does he try
To lull to peace this world of wrong?

Oh, cricket! You bring dreamland near!
You fill my mind with thoughts of love
And prayers that on earth may appear
The calm that comes from Him above

The dreams your cricket songs produce
Are dreams of smiling, laughing faces.
The cares that in the day run loose
Are lost in happy, dancing places.

Oh cricket, strum your lullaby,
Don't stop your soporific song!
Your music is a distant sign
Of that fair land and happy throng.

MARCH   Carol Lentz

I am the month of March, the beginning of spring.
I bring the first warm winds after the long, cold winter.
I breathe new life to all that is dead.
Somedays I am fierce like a lion and tangle the kites
                    in the tree tops,
Always I am kind to the flowers and grasses
                    which are struggling up through the ground.
My days are longer with sunshine, which prepares the earth
                    for the first spring rain.
I awake nature from her winter's sleep.
I am March.

WEST ROCK, NEW HAVEN   Patricia Ann Nizen

Royal and rusty and radiant she stands,
Silent and stately in the sun's shimmering gleam.

High in the heavens the hawks soar and dive,
Over her forests of regal trees.

Beautiful and bubbling her brooks tumble over
The rocks, round and rough, that make up their beds.

Slowly the sun to silver turns,
Crowning her crest with a glorious light.

Glowing she glorifies God's great handiwork,
Free from the frustrations and fears of men.

DAWN   Dorothy Anne Godfrey

Tingling salt air
Caressing my face,
Soft, foamy waves
In my embrace.

As streams the glory
Of the eastern sky,
From diamond waters
The sun rose high.

Down at the shore,
Dawn on the sea,
God's greatest creation
Gave faith to me!

A POEM   Bonnie Amrich

A poem is a lovely thing
To glorify the birth of Spring;
To tell of Winter's heavenly snow;
To whisper about the moonlight's glow;
To create an illusion of wondrous things --
A silvery star, an angel's ring,
The rainbow's prism, a halo sweet,
And the green grass a carpet for Nature's feet.

RHAPSODY   Pat Janis

Free! - running, skipping through open fields,
As does the hare or the lamb.
Rosy-cheeked youth, hair tussling with the wind,
Arms waving freely.
Calling to nature - the sky - all mankind;
Animals join the chase;
Child of man, bird and beast playing together.
Distance - direction ne'er a concern;
The fields are endless - endless to the sky.
Hills, valleys, fields blend together,
Still there is no fatigue.
Even the swallow lingers behind;
Yet youth, inspired by freedom and joy,
Overtakes the fleeing clouds.

SUMMER VALLEY   Marla Kay Unruh

The cloudless skies are now deep blue,
Pierced by snow-tipped turrets
Which rise majestically above
The sun-kissed hills and valleys.

The little hamlet preens itself
In its lake blue mirror,
While winds come through and through green pines
And wave the valley grasses.

A little riv'let scampers by
Flaunting foam lace dresses,
While clamb'ring down the rocky stair
To join with other waters.

DEAD TREE   Ruth Jones

       Stark and bare against a cloud-blown sky, it stands,
Reaching its brittle, leafless arms in mute appeal
For its green, departed soul.
Storm-beaten, sun-warmed, it has known life and spring.
Now old, alone, stripped of bark,
Its surface worn smooth and gray,
It still reaches higher.
So must we, when despair has kidnapped hope
Keep groping upward, however blindly,
Though we make stiff figures of patient solitude.

A LOST GENERATION   Robert Czerwinski

Destined for a few,
Avoided by others,
Insensible of some.
The noumenon of the unknown,
Savage fears float through the mind
Like gossamer.
Beliefs of horror rise.
Persons and things of doubtful origin appear.
Those hidden deep reach forth.
Insane ideas are inscribed on the
Mind by sharp cutting ghost.
Madness comes,
Dreaded by some,
Bliss to others.

MOTHER'S CROCHETING   Nancy Binns

The pretties my Mother crochets,
   Are to me, works of art
For she determinedly blends
   Every intricate part.

To work and make money,
   Is a trite old line
But I'd rather, like Mother,
   Make something fine.

Yes, money and time
   Soon go their ways
But Mom creates beauty
   When she crochets!

INSPIRATION   Peggy Jones

The cowled monk upon the mantle stands
Above the sins of man, serenely lone,
His face toward God - yet in his outstretched hands
The rosary in prayers for man moves on.
What artist wise beyond the ways of men,
Inspired by every thought in life that's good
And fine, remembered heaven once again,
And then created this wise saint from wood?
For passersby who gaze upon his face,
Uplifted by his gentle piety,
Reflect upon their lives, then stand abased
By their own conduct's impropriety.
The artist builded better than he knew,
For many has this figure guided true.

THE GIVER OF GIFTS   Jean Washington

God gave me life,
A gift, no human being could give
God gave me faith,
That I may seek beyond the life I live,
God gave me the world
Full of the wonders He has done,
But the best gift that God gave me
Was the Mother of His Son.

PARENTS' LOVE   Roberta Sell

They may not have diamonds,
They may not have gold,
But they have the one thing
That will never grow old.

It cannot be stolen
It cannot be bought
It can only be given
To the ones who have fought

For the love of their neighbors,
For the love of their land,
And the glories of Jesus
So they can live again.

FRAMES   Dottie Cotner

Life is a painting.
You may blend into it
Every color of the rainbow.
But the only difference between
Your picture and anyone else's
Is the frame you put it in.

THE SPIDER WEB   Fay Yeatts

'Twas only a spider's web I saw,
But it was free of every flaw.

It was made of silver lace
And each silver thread in the right place.

It was sprinkled with gold
Ah, 'twas lovely to behold.

To me it seems most strange that one should fear
The little spider, who with so much care

Has spun this beauty for us to see,
For without him the spider web could never be.

WHITE DAISIES   Theresa Gajderowicz

White daisies on a field of green,
Simplicity in this pleasant scene
Touches the heart with its silent grace.
Dreams living on from place to place.

Each petal linked in precious gold,
A thought tucked in each gentle fold.
Dewdrops of yellow amid virginal white,
Peaks through the green like the stars of night.

Lovers of this flower pluck
Wishing it would bring them luck.
Purity is its utmost meaning.
Upward .... toward God they're leaning.

Many years have come and gone
But, true, the daisy still lives on.
Flower, fairest of them all,
Are you ready for my call?

SONNET ON UNCONVENTIONALITY   Alvin L. Gregg

Since I have lived a score of years on earth,
My lot has been to seem like all my peers.
I've found it hard to give myself to mirth
Or to forsake my life to sobbing tears:
Which fact could ne'er raise me above the plane.
If I desire to leave behind all fears
And make myself evince great might and main:
My own delights or bent should breathe forth jeers
At what my fellows hold to be quite sane;
My heart must give to strange ideas birth,
My mind all fetters forged before disdain,
My work cause seas to tremble from my firth.
To give myself unlimited delight
I must irradiate man's wonted night.

LOVE   Elliot A. Ryan

When winter's gone and spring is blest,
When flowers start to climb,
When birds begin to build their nests,
When church bells start to chime,
So tender little voices seem,
And love appears in youth.
All hearts begin the age old scheme
Because they know the truth.
Though love a man cannot define,
He knows that it is there.
Without a word or outward sign
It fills the springtime air.

FALL   George Straub

I still remember many a lovely fall,
Leaves piled high 'long a fence or wall,
With apples fallen, over ripe,
A lovely red against the gray tile pipe.

In the barnyard, hay piled high,
With hungry stock standing by,
With hair heavy and quite thick,
For Winter which is coming quick.

Hunters in the fields of corn,
Distant shots like the sound of a horn,
To point out pheasants where they hide.
My faithful hunter at my side.

LAKE ERIE   Maxine Ambus

Wind when it blows is my lover,
But the water is more faithful.
The water is always there
Stolidly raging or serene, translucent;
Complement to a mood.
Wind will deliberately die.
There were nights when I walked far to stay with wind,
And it left me farthest from home.
I stood beside water.
Now water will be my solace:
The water is faithful;
But the wind, when it blows, will be my love.

CHAMELEON CLOUDS   Marilyn Goen

Fluffy lambs up in the blue
With snowy fleece and outline true;
Frisking on an azure meadow
Their playmates only the winds that blow.
Once I saw a bloodhound grim
Pointing its nose at the heaven's rim;
Then down the hill looking o'er the plain
I saw a sure sign of gathering rain,
A bleak, blustering, billowy black;
Then the thunder sounded with a noisy crack;
The big black clouds were wolves at prey
The rain took over and got its way.

YONDER HILL   Allen Govin

Won't you come with me to yonder hill
By the fields of golden grain,
And listen to the bluebird's song
And the howling rumble of a train?
Oh, the train is far off somewhere
Letting you know it's coming through,
But the bluebird's song which you dearly love,
Is also rolling in the sky so blue.
So won't you come to yonder hill
By the fields of golden grain,
And know the world as I do there
With peaceful song and sound of train?

SPRING IS A LOVELY LADY Ross Crow

Winter is old, and bent, and gray.
(He seemed a youth of genius, rare.)
Despise him, reject him, turn him away.
(He came with promises, fair.)

He's bent and ugly; his beard's made hoary with snow.
Greet him with a jeer.
Curse him and beat him, make him go.
(He came with a promise of cheer.)

The pale moon is waning, and hides 'neath a cloud.
The birds hail his going with twittering song.
Joy accompanies his funereal shroud,
And the winds come swiftly to drive him along.

So, make him leave us,
Destroy his emblem, the snow he hurled.
He tried to deceive us.
But Spring is a lovely lady, courted by all the world.

DAWN Dolores Petch

The moon has watched over you,
In the darkness of the night.
As the light slips over the horizon
The sky lights up once more,
With a wondrous glow.
The lake simmers
As the color skimmers,
Touching you with the warmth
Of that glow.
Now, Dawn with its warm and motherly sun
Will keep you in comfort,
As you see the arising of Dawn.

SNOWBOUND CITY Rubyjean Landsman

City with your smoke stacks high,
'scrapers lined against the sky;
Houses stiff in formal rows,
Drab and dismal in repose.
City with your bustling crowd,
And your noises shrill and loud;
With each narrow, cluttered street,
Laid in colorless concrete.
Suddenly transformed , you tower
As though by some magic power;
As beneath a cloak of snow,
Strangely soft and still you grow.

THE PEARL DIVERS   Muriel Barber

Come, come, let us drift with the outflowing tide;
Along on the billows of surf let us ride.
Now down deep, deep down to the bottom of the sea
Away from the cares of the world would we flee
For the silvery vapor caressing the skin
Soothes the gentle pulsation rising within.

Of sound all is void; dull silence prevails.
Through blurry fluid follow the air bubble trails
To pink coral castles of limestone and pearl
Where hues of blue-green give a dizzying whirl.
With treasure we rise to where surf will unwreathe;
Our spent diaphragms warn that humans must breathe.

SUMMER   Beverly Kinney

Red roses blooming in the summer air
Tell me of that love still true
You and I had long ago, with fair
Red roses blooming.

The clouds above us cast a warning blue;
But we, unheedful, came to care -
And we were forced to say adieu.

I wish with all my heart that where
You are, I could be too.
Remember the love we have, and rare
Red roses blooming.

HIS HAND HAS LED ME
Shirley Goldfinger

When the painful hand of sadness
Prepares to lead me
Into the deep abyss of grief
The comforting quiet of the night
           Appeases me.
The spectral sadness
Disappears mysteriously . . .
           His hand has led me.

When the ghost of skepticism
Prepares to lead me
Into the darkling realm of disbelief
I see the petals of a rose
And believe again . . .
           His hand has led me.

TO A ROSE   Richard Hernandez

Blushing princess, why is yours the freshest smile?
What wondrous dream blesses you with everlasting cheer?
What great secret guides your life through a medley
                              of thrilling song?
Does your gaiety reflect a gentle view of life?
Is the secret your melodious communion with
                              the good earth?
Is your noble dream a hope for tomorrow?
No! These gifts are but a coin from a wealth of hidden treasure!
O maiden of fable, grow into a more inspiring miracle.
Live! Live to be adored as you were meant to be?

I AM MUSIC   JoAnne Petersen

I am music!
I come as do the soft, sweet, spring breezes;
And as rolling thunder, I descend on my listeners.
One minute I am as a kite in a high, windy sky,
The next, I am music spilled from clouds and
                              plunging stars.
Fire one moment, and ice the next;
I am made from hope, love and understanding.
Yes, all these things am I; for
I am music!

WEARY WINTER   Faye Ann Lowe

The dark, bare branches stand
Against the steel-grey sky
Clutching, clutching like a hand
At the wind whistling by.

Barren and bleak are they:
No beauty do they possess,
But winter leads on to May
And summer brings out the best.

So it is with life
As we go from day to day,
Struggling in our strife
To lead the righteous way.

Many winters we waver through
And many sorrows they bring,
But standing staunch and true
Behold! At last comes spring!

A QUESTION   Molly Scott

Were I a tree
With branch and limb
Strong and well from birth,
With leaf that rustles in the wind
Like song of unseen mirth,
With roots that strive to hold the earth
Within their porous grasp,
Would I have joy, would I have love,
Would I know peace at last?

THE SONG OF A CHILD   Thelma Van Wyk

A fancy note of sweet refrain
    Is music to the ears,
But let a child sing very plain
    And to our eyes come tears.

It may not be a change of words
    But just a change of sound,
That keeps the very words we heard
    So far beyond reknown.

The people gather round in groups
    To hear a singer grand,
But smaller groups have larger hopes
    To see beginners stand.

Remember when you hear the choice
    Of people far and near,
That none quite like the child's sweet voice
    Can make it sound so dear.

THE SINISTER WAVE   Yvonne Philipp

Just like a thief at night,
With fingers cold as ice,
He comes in all his might
To lap against the shore
And smash what comes his way!
Then gives a mighty roar
And moves back out to sea.
This monster comes and goes -
Uncaught we let him be
To roam the ocean wide
And bring on deathly fear
With each new coming tide!

THE THERMOMETER   Ann Zimmerman

It is a slave to mankind -
Laboring in the sweat of July
Or in the fleeting cold of the winter season -
Tall and slender like a wooden pole.
Its crimson blood bursts forth
In a narrow stream,
Waiting for the sunlight to cast its glow
On the cut glass.
Once created, it toils continually -
The thermometer

IN THE HALL OF THE MOUNTAIN KING

Ellsworth Wheeler

Suddenly, stealthily, out and about us,
Come to the nerves the increasing vibrations
Of bass viols and cellos in unison chorus.

Rising and soaring the theme surges onward,
Until we imagine a horrible sight
Of goblins a-dancing in fiendish delight.

And now the finale that makes our ears ring,
Chord upon chord and robustly it ends
In the Hall of the Mountain King!

THE LEAF   Mary Ellen Quirk

The leaf leaped lightly
To the ground.
She laughed a bit,
And danced around.

Arrayed in a gown
Of red-gold hue,
She powdered her face
In the morning dew.

Winking at a rose,
Then teasing a bee,
She rested at the feet
Of a scarlet oak tree.

Don't you know
O leaf so small,
That pride doth come
Before the fall?

THE FURIES   Gloria Heineke

Blow on, fierce monarch of the sky!
But thou cannot surpass this fury in my heart.
A fiercer blast beats here in my soul,
More so, than thou can e'er impart.

Oh death! Sweet death!
Come to me and still my living breath.
Is not a bud that blooms among the thorn
Better left unbloomed or left unborn?

THE STORM   Richard Kieffer

The storm was fierce, the wind a gale.
The rain had turned to balls of hail.
Darkness hovered in the skies.
Ravens raised their horror cries.
Trees, their heads bent down with fear,
Cowered to the stone wall near.
The sea, it lashed and rolled and roared,
The waves again, a mighty hoard.
Through this Wildness a young girl came
Looking for some one. She called his name.
Hearing no answer, she advanced still.
Her damp cloak around her, she shivered with chill.
Then she saw him, and with her last breath,
Ran to his side for a meeting with Death.

A GARDEN   Adrienne Hebbeler

Rocky cliffs climb up the hill,
As a mountain steep,
Graceful little daffodils,
Form a pattern neat.

Honeysuckle winds its way
Round a picket fence,
Big red roses in gentle sway
Are soldiers on defense.

Winter nears and brings its fears,
And soil then soon will harden,
Till summer calls, O flowers dear,
Sleep will hover o'er your garden.

GOD'S NAME IN VAIN   Aithel McMahon

Why use His name in madness vain,
When you yourself, you only stain.
But good to Him in every race,
To keep His name in sacred grace.

INCONGRUITY   Hollis Goldberg

Pink as the blush of angels
    Tiny wild flowers bloomed,
While below the rocky ledges
    Angry breakers boomed.

The barren cliffs of granite
    They covered, wild and free.
How strange to see such beauty
    By the cold, relentless sea!

No witchcraft could produce them
    No charm nor magic ring,
It was God's will that grew them,
    Through the miracle of spring.

IMMORTALITY   Kenneth Edwards

There is a view broader than that you see;
There is a haven where everyone is free.
There is a place where battle-ridden souls may go;
We call it death, 'tis immortality.

The seeming endless sleep which we call death,
It is but birth, where the soul is set free.
At a thing called death, we bow our heads and weep;
Don't weep at death, 'tis immortality.

Go my friend, 'twill not be very long;
Your work is done and peace rest with thee.
Your works and thoughts will always live on,
For this is nothing but immortality.

Go my friend, life winds and turns,
He'll lead you forth from your troubled sea;
For you have learned what every man should know,
Don't speak of death, say immortality.

THE HARVEST   Rosemary Fidele

Take a walk through the meadows of yesteryear
Into the fields of today.
And harvest your faults and virtues
As a farmer harvests his hay.

Then thresh the faults into tiny sins
As a farmer threshes his grain.
And plow them deep down into the ground
So they'll never be seen again.

And the crop that remains when these jobs are done
Should never know anger nor strife,
For they're sure they're ready for market,
The market of everday life.

AUTUMN   Geraldyne Amore

Hazy meadows blue with smoke
Autumn fires of country folk
All along the forest trails
Green of trees and rosebud fails
Gentians closing firm and tight
Fairer far than daisies white
Fades the red of the evening sky
But autumn to me will never die.

SONG   Martha Ann Detamore

Has the summer come without the rose,
Or left the bird behind?
Is the blue changed above thee,
O world! or am I blind?

Will you change every flower that grows,
Or only change this spot,
Where she who said, "I love thee,"
Now says, "I love thee not."

The skies seemed true above thee;
The rose true on the tree
The bird seemed true the summer through
But all proved false to me.

INSUFFICIENT   Margaret Renshaw

Justice is not enough, we must have mercy;
Knowledge is not enough, we must have faith; -
The tangible things are not enough in life,
            They are sufficient only in death.

PO' LI'L TU'KEY   Ann Walker

Po' li'l tu'key
A settin' in de straw
Ain' got no notion whut you for.

Li'l tu'key you
            bin fed and fed
'til you' coxcomb am a
            bright, bright red.

Play li'l tu'key
gobble an' eat,
For tomorrow on de table
You is MEAT!

OH WEAVING VINE OF LOVE
                        Sylvia D. Sollien
            Oh, weaving vine of love,
Why dost thou choke me so?
            And whisper to me of love's song,
In tones so sweet and low?

            Why dost thou twine thy leafy vines
Around my heart so weak,
            And make me love him all the more,
Even though I be meek?

            Thou canst make me happy,
And thou canst make me sad,
            And fill my heart with seething hatred
Till it drives me mad.

            Oh, weaving vine of love
Lift thy clinging vines!
            And free me of this eternal love
And all that it entwines.

SIN   Donald Rehder

I am greed, filth, scorn, and hatred.
I use foul language and injure people's hearts.
I steal, beg, rob and cheat to get the things I desire.
I strangle, stab, beat and slay my victims.
I use all the forces of the World, Death, and the Devil.
I lie, deceive, conjure and curse.
I am omnipresent and work all hours.
I crave poison, guns, knives, darts and gases.
I am out to get all, no matter what the price.
I am untrustworthy, disloyal, and not helpful.
I am disobedience, and Anti-Christian.
I am SIN.

THE WILLOW   Sylvia Specker

"A wisp of beauty" is the willow tree
    When swayed by the breath of spring.
    Its leaves dance forth like waves of the sea.

"A wisp of beauty" is the willow tree.
    It often weeps like you or me.
    Then from its branches sweet melodies sing.

"A wisp of beauty" is a willow tree
    When swayed by the breath of spring.

BABY   Barbara Heim

A whisper of angels,
A thought from above,
Look! Oh see! A bundle of love.

Chubby hands
Curled like an unbloomed rose.
Blue eyes
Twinkling as if he knows
That all around him people gather near
To hear his funny gurgles -
Music to the ear.

A whisper of angels,
A thought from above,
This is a baby! A miracle of love!

DAY AND NIGHT   Sharon Green

The sun shines upon my window pane
          To rouse me from a world of dreams,
While birds sing in sweet refrain.
          The day begins in its usual way -
          The barking of dogs, honking of horns.

Night creeps slowly in
Soundless but not sightless.
The sun slowly falls
Behind the trees and buildings.
Finally all is quiet
Except the hooting of an owl
And twinkling of the stars.

GAY AUTUMN   Edna Vondracek

Autumn's here; I know it now.
Her shining hair's the cob-webbed sky;
A morning's frost, the twinkle in her eye;
Her colored dress the swaying bough.

She brings with her the gifts of fall,
The crackling cornstalks, pumpkin pie,
Bittersweet, and ducks that fly,
Acorns, hickory nuts and all.

She stays a while, then moves away.
Her absence brings Old North Wind cold,
With snowy winter, fierce and bold.
It makes us miss young Autumn gay.

LIFE IS LIKE A BLACKBOARD
          Martha Jane Claney

Life is like a blackboard,
Except - the Words written on a blackboard
May be removed by the flick of an eraser.

In life, we find no eraser
To remove the marks we make
As we move from day to day.
And many things we would
Wipe out, if we had a chance!

But on our blackboard of life,
Every mistake remains visible
Until the board is washed clean
By our Death.

LOVE   Kathleen Ward

The frowning clouds of gloom
Settled slowly over the desert;
And the parched mouth of the land cried out,
And the tired and hungry arms of the land reached up,
Beseeching the god of the ominous clouds,
Imploring the god of the ominous clouds,
To free it from its suffering.
But he looked down at the writhing, aching body
                              of the desert,
And laughed, the biting laugh of power;
And, gathering about him his thick grey robes,
He moved slowly on, unyielding.
And the desert spit out its heart and died.

YOUTH GOES NOT ASTRAY   Donna Trolinger

Here in this world of godlessness and greed
Sore torn with murders vile and wild misdeeds
Youth knows not what shall be his life of creed.
Each man's advice both good and bad he heeds.
In puzzlement he knows not which to choose.
If he but tread the pathway wrong and then
Astray does go, his chance he will soon lose,
And shameful live, scorned by more noble men,
But youth with ideals strong goes not astray.
He searcheth not in vain for God and truth.
Self-sacrifice his goal, not gold array.
Thank God, our youth do choose the honest way
That makes the world more liveable each day.

CODA   Cynthia Elizabeth Carso

I have met the hungry faces
In hollow rooms, in vestibules of trains,
Met them coming and going along dusty streets,
Dragging nervous heels through littered parks.
I have seen them, hollow-eyed and empty,
Rat-like, their eyes in the shadows.
I have met them and passed by,
But known the cold hurt of those faces
That cry for recognition in the fleet moment
Before the fear comes down over their eyes,
And they draw to them, shuddering,
The old hate.

CHEERING WORDS (from an Officer to his Men in Korea)   Robert Klawitter

The bees kissed the daisies one clear summer day,
And the sun warmed the sky for the breezes to play.
My heart skipped a beat, and I whistled a tune
As I walked with my love in the bright month of June.

Yes, life is so sweet and the hour so dear
When you are young and your sweetheart is near,
So think of that time, and forget all your fear
As we march (slush, slush) on through the mud.

A little white house on a little green hill,
A dream come to life, and all is still
Save the quivering buds of the lilac with song
From the wild orchestra as it twitters along.

No, the world's not so pretty, nor its songs so sweet
As you lie on the ground with death at your feet,
Weary of work, sick of defeat, so -- --
Fight on to the time you go home.

Oh, you men so true and men so great,
That would charge on to the arms of fate,
Live now in hope till you can celebrate
The victory of love.

DAWN-DREAM   Paula Stahl

Dawn stretched her fingers
        through the sun
And made her mural painting.
Flowers yawned;
        Their leaves where dewdrops clung
        a jeweled scene creating,
And all the while, in bed I lay
        Wrapped up in amber shading.

MOONLIGHT SONATA   Constance Reynolds

My eyes are cast down
With lovelorn sorrow
The sad light of the moon
Caresses my brow.
I love for no tomorrow.
I dream of no paradise.
I weep in the stillness
Of the night.

BEAUTY   Sheila Doyle

That I should know the beauty of the day
Shall be my prayer as I arise each morn,
To see the miracles of nature, small and large,
As beginning day moves into place;
The darkness slowly giving way to light
The reddening sky heralding the dawn
The flaming sun moving upward in the heavens
The birds setting up a chorus of welcome akin to
                    that of the angels.
Oh, to be worthy of it all; for if worthy, then
I shall know the beauty of each day.

YOUTH   Clive E. Driver

I was youth.
I walked upon a hill at midnight.
I looked up at the stars,
At the lights of the city far below.
Each taper pointed out the road that I must take;
Each gleam a dream, a hope,
Some to be fulfilled in joy,
Some to be denied in pain.
The gentle winds gave me strength, courage, inspiration,
I took the path with faith.

LIVE YOUR FREEDOM! DON'T DIE FOR IT!
                    Shirley Fielder
Fight for freedom,
    Die for peace!
Or live in freedom
    That wars may cease!

March to battle!
    Start a war!
Or try understanding
    War no more!

Kill the enemy,
    New ones arise!
Make them our friends
    The enemy dies!

Die for your country
    And mankind no more!
Live your freedom
    We're here evermore!

AWARENESS   Margaret Mealing

The teacher read the poem that I had written to the class,
The thoughts which came to me as I had led my pencil on the paper,
The feelings that were close and part of me alone -
My eyes hurriedly followed down the lines of a foreign work,
Yet only knowing what sounded from the teacher's lips as words.
As I listened, my eyes unseeing what I saw,
Pleased but frightened by a thing akin to painful self-awareness
Yet conscious not of self but only of my words -
But how can I explain that words are more than words.

I HEARD   Betty Lou Seifrid

Did you ever hear a sound
That you never heard at all?
Are you certain no vibrations
Reached tympanic wall?

What is it then, that makes you turn,
Precisely at this very instance,
To see a butterfly settle down upon a rose?
Did you hear its footsteps? From this distance?

What is it then, that awakens you,
In the middle of the night?
The calm before the storm is ---
Is quiet at its height!

There is only One, Who can cry aloud,
And never make a sound;
I could not hear half what I do,
If God were not around!

THE SHINING SUN   Jaymee Griffiths

I saw the sun's rays shining through
The snowy clouds on a morning new;
This light poured down on everything,
It sparkled on a robin's wing.

It danced upon my window sill,
And in the light the world was still;
It touched each glist'ning drop of dew
That lay on flowers of every hue.
White clouds sailed through the pale blue sky;
Alone in the world were God and I.

RARE MOMENTS Mydra McGriff

Dusk comes softly, slowly, almost without notice,
The warm glow of light from my room casts a golden ray,
The small bits of delicate lace edged in the fine cut
                              crystals of ice
Catch the glimmer and twinkle as a thousand stars
                      through the grey shadows
As they fall to be claimed by the Mother Earth.
All is hush. Do not speak. Do not think. But dream.
Capture these moments of enchantment, guard them well,
For they are few and their presence sweet.

GOD'S MESSENGER TO MAN James Paul

On the shadows of the glistening sun
My thoughts do meditate;
Until my heart from contemplation turns,
To that everlasting flow of nature round about.

The trees swaying softly 'gainst the sky,
Their tops all gold and green;
Take my thoughts to yesterdays,
To things that might have been.

The birds and streams all sing with glee,
And bring to mind the joy at hand;
When nature in all her glory speaks to me,
"O am God's messenger to man."

SUNBEAMS AND SHADOWS
                              Marilyn S. Jarabines

"How fresh the air is after rain!"
                A simple soul's remark;
"Bah! fun is spoil'd and all is vain,"
                The pessimist did bark.

"'Tis time to rise and work once more,"
                The optimist did note.
"Alas, to work at unliked chore
                I'd rather sit and gloat."

Be wise my friends and listen well
                This lesson do you learn -
With sunbeams many shadows dwell
                So happiness with trials you earn.

DELIGHT   Elizabeth Hoagland

It is so hard to find the words to say,
How my love for life grows each day,
So filled am I with sweet delight,
As I watch Day join hands with Night;
Each sparrow sings his song for me alone
A melody fine, seasoned with rich, warm tone,
The emerald span of the old earth's breast
Carpets the floor 'tween high white crests;
My loved ones, all so vital in my life
Each one helps to lessen burden and strife.
Azure skies cover this bright gay earth;
Life is carried on in death and birth;
How filled am I with life's way,
As my love for life grows each day.

WISDOM   Donna Diekoff

Wisdom
is like a gnarled, old apple tree:

it feels the first, faint breath of rosy dawn;
it knows the gladness of joy-filtered sunshine;
it has been drenched with sober autumn rain,
Time's tears; has laughed with April's playful thunder;
it has grown sage with knowledge of the wind;
it knows the thrill of flowing, pulsing sap,
that gives it life;
it has known snow in spring;
it knows the peace and magnitude of stars,
those twinkling hosts that tell man what God is;
and yet, it knows the sureness and the strife,
the birth, the death, and life in clods of earth ...

Wisdom is even so.

SONNET ON IMMORTAL WORDS
                              Kenneth Warwick

In the season's growth of gibberish,
That soon dies with unborn seeds,
Buds a visage of the future;
Blooms a wisdom more than weeds;
Words pried open prematurely,
Still pre-seasoned strong as steel,
Words whose wealth knows no absorbtion,
Words Time's frost cannot congeal.

What's the root of their existence,
'Neath their ample fruit of thought,
When we pluck them from our memory
And they strive as green as aught?
'Tis a germ, God-sown, that's giving
Ceaseless guidance we have sought.

THE MOUNTAINS   Alan Schweissinger

As I reflect upon my mountains dear
I sadly miss the Freedom Nature gives
In quietude and peace and skies so clear,
In wooded heights where every blessing lives.
I oft relive those days I spent in fun:
I run across the hills to meadows green
And climb to snow-capped peaks all-bathed in sun
Where all the world below me can be seen.
The small log cabin, full of Friendship old,
Lies still beside the softly flowing stream.
Such memories are worth far more than gold,
And happiness throughout my life will gleam
That I of this great scene have played a part;
A thankfulness to God now fills my heart.

LONELINESS   Diane Archer

Loneliness is not
A face,
                    stark, pale;
Wearing grief blatantly,
A poor mask
For all
                    to see.

Loneliness is
A mouth
                    over-painted;
Laughing too loud -
And empty eyes
That search
                    the crowd.

HASTY HEART   Doris Langford

O hasty heart, begone from me;
Why hast thou hurt me so?
I loved and laughed, but far too quick
My love, now there he goes.

O why did'st thou deceive me?
What did I do so wrong?
Alas, I know, 'tis well I know,
Why sadness is my song.

Why was I oh so hasty?
Why are we now apart?
'Tis known so well that sadness
Is borne in a hasty heart.

THE LAST HOPE   Sue Elstein

Turbulence revolves in my brain;
Stormy thoughts, clouded veils,
Shake reality from its roots.
To be unsure of the sublime, even as
One's heart is tightly shut,
Is pitiful. One may see beauty,
But not recognize it
Dashed against paths of thorns
Where dreams lie in fear, unable
To blossom and unable to soothe.

I TRIED TO WRITE A POEM   Vincent Martin

I tried to write a poem
Of the glittering moon
On an ebon night,
The lustrous ocean,
Or the elusive wind,
Of the rustling grass,
The musical trees.
I grew discouraged
With my futile efforts,
Since words can't substitute
For nature itself.

MY TREASURE CHEST   Thelma Eicher

I have a treasure chest - my heart -
Where all my memories I store.
Shattered dreams and loneliness share a part,
Happy times, old friends and more.

When I have nothing else on hand,
I unwrap time and loose the band.
I've remembered things that others forget.
I spin dreams to fulfill yet.

Times that once were but are now past,
Times that once were; but only memories last.
Friends that once were, but now are gone
And all that remains is friendship's bond.

But now time beckons and I must go
On to find more treasures so,
I can put them safely away
To reminisce another day.

TO THE SOUTHWINDS   June Horner

Blow thou balmy southwids, caress the tempest blue
            'Til the coral beneath her realms,
Is scattered like the dew.

Pound, thou foamy southseas, upon the diamond sands,
            And bring to them that magic
Of remote, enchanted lands.

Here, in the pungent salt air, with trouble far away,
            Where dawn dispells all darkness
I should like to stay.

BERMUDA MEMORIES   Diana Joell

I wish to be by waters crystal deep,
And see the flash of glistening spray fly high,
To stand aloft on many a windswept steep
And gaze above to heights of bright blue sky.

The sand so clear of gleaming pink and white,
The shimmering water adding touch of blue
The sun in heaven whose rays are now so bright,
Give to the sand and sky a pastel hue.

The fragrant scent of lilies grown in May,
The freshness of the breezes straight from sea
The glory of a cloudless summer day,
Or tropic night moonlit for us to see.

All these are memories tranquil, strong and clear,
Among the things in life I hold most dear.

BEAUTY   Barbara Courtney

There's beauty all around our paths
    Because God's Hand has formed
Each fluttering leaf and rosy bloom
    The earth's rich soil has warmed.

There's beauty in the ocean depths,
    And on the mountain peak.
There's beauty in the city,
    And in the forest deep.

God speaks through every flower
    That opens in the Spring.
Through all the beauty of His earth
    His blessings there may ring.

HIGHLIGHTS   Bonnie Seeman

Oh, the dark and mellow hue
Of a pansy flecked with dew,
Whose pithy stem holds up
Its face, to see the molten color
Of a lovely butter-cup.
Above, the loquat spreads its waxy, brittle leaves
And the singing of the springtime
Is the rustling of the trees.

THE CAT   Benita Jane Blitzer

Like silent velvet, moving slowly,
    Like April moons in orbits old,
His eyes with blackened centers staring,
    The eye itself a yellow gold.
The paws that creep in dusky splendor
    The tail that waves to rhythms slow.
Perhaps a hint of Cleopatra
    Whose ruby, diamond jewels doth glow.
A statue shining, all black marble
    The cat in splendor now doth stand
A king, the conqueror of nations,
    Aloof to every human hand.

THE CATHEDRAL   David Clayson

There stands amidst the city's drone,
A symphony of glass and stone,

A building great, whose towers point
To heaven for God's hand to annoint.

For this cathedral tall and nate,
Is man's own gift to all that's great.

Within, beneath the arches tall,
The rainbow lights dance through the hall,

Across the imaged saints of old
To stop upon the altars gold.

Where priests intone their love of God,
And laymen with their aves nod.

For here the spirit of God does dwell,
And here all men in piety swell.

LOST   Marie Roach

I loved him;
My heart and soul were his.

Somewhere, on a distant shore,
The rocks and sand lie fading in the sun.
His agony is over; mine has just begun.

I loved him.
But he is gone ...

THE THOUGHT   Margaret A. Gruner

Today it is the thought
Which is of importance.
The phrasing little matters -
Only the bare, naked chain of the elemental thought;
For a valuable thought will only be lessened
By the gingerbread of useless words,
But a meaningless void can be
Worshipped if cleverly clothed.
Think out your code and ever after
Adhere to it; only first,
Think.

THE SEASONS   Carole Stevens

Flowers in pale yellow and warm pink,
Grass, cool, green and alive,
Angry yet gentle winds ....
Spring and the rebirth of nature.

Joy and love in their fullest are blooming,
Youth is spreading its wings,
Towns are alive and moving,
Summer has come once again.

Deep browns, rich reds, and bright yellows,
Nature, a true artist's in her glory,
Paints her masterpiece of color ...
Autumn, the harvest time of God's splendor.

Snow, white and clean; ice, clear as crystal;
Tinkling sleigh bells; and children's gay laughter.
Somber, lovely hymns, and joyous, praising
                                    carols ...
Winter with its cold beauty and stark bareness.

THE GREATEST TRAGEDY   Joan Bennett

Within the depths of my heart, a storm gathers momentum.
Hatred clouds my soul and happiness is a phantom
Chased by winds of stark, bleak tragedy;
Dangerous clouds of rebellion rise within me.
"Heed nought," cries my heart, "let the winds will thy fate."
Yet all the while, my soul cries out, "alas, too late,
                    too late."
A threatening roll of thunder drowns the last faint plea;
The storm breaks and tragedy sweeps down to engulf me.
Too late I realize the dangerous ground I trod;
Too late, I reach with my wind-swept soul to grasp
                    the hand of God.

OTHERS   Diane Pedersen

When, in the cycle of human strife
It becomes a man to woe,
When Doubt hovers o'er his future life
And he trusts neither friend nor foe,

Then is the time for him to fly
Unto the top-most peak
And see the troubles that have passed him by
Because they had others to seek.

SUNSET   Johnye Faye Storey

I lift mine eyes unto the west
    And there I do behold
The sun is reddening the sky;
    With bliss it fills my soul.

It makes me think of things unknown
    To man and his weak mind --
Of things that God alone can make
    Of things that are divine.

I see the mountains blue with night
    Their shadowy hues entwine;
Dry cones and twigs are rustling as
    The breeze blows through the pine.

The flowers gently nod their heads
    To bid the sun goodnight;
It slowly drops behind the hills;
    At last it's out of sight.

THREE TENSES   Kay Kapfer

Yesterday, a carefree child ran, laughing gaily, in my place;
Today, an adolescent, I, laughing carelessly, ponder
                    problems just beyond my grasp.

Tomorrow, who will fill my slippers?
A worn old woman, laughing mirthlessly?
Or a lovely lady, musing, laughing kindly at some past
                    childish fancy?

AFTERMATH   Betty Williams

A wilted corsage -
A crushed formal -
Both stained with tears.
These are all that remain of a night,
One that should have been filled with happiness.
I tasted the nectar of happiness once
But its sweetness has grown bitter -
For I loved him and he didn't love me.

REACHING HEAVEN   Marjory Davis

In the meadow I shall wander,
To seek a hidden land;
In the valley I shall walk,
To find God's land.

On the grass I shall run,
To feel the promise of Spring;
On the sidewalks of New York
I shall lift my heart and sing.

On the river bank I shall stand,
To smell the clean, fresh air;
On a cloud I shall kneel,
To hear an angel's prayer.

On Someone's kind smile,
I shall reach the stars and moon;
On Someone's loving heart,
I shall reach heaven soon.

Then as I walk on a sea of clouds,
I shall see my illusions come true,
For everything that I feel down here
I shall feel again, with you.

FIVE-MONTH TANTRUM Patricia Oliver

At the crest of the hill where all winds meet
In November, to hold their election
They try not to be frightened by Boreas' threats
Of revenge, if he's not their selection.

They cast their ballots, and hold their breaths,
Then shiver and shake from the blast,
As Boreas finds he's defeated again,
And they all get away from there - fast.

THE DANCE OF THE FLOWERS Mary Claire Buzek

Sweet Rose has donned a gown of red,
    Upon this happy day;
Gay Mum has placed upon her head
    A cap of golden spray;
Tall black-eyed Susan shyly nods
    To shapely Daffodil;
While graceful Blue-Bell's tiny feet
    Tap lightly to each trill.
Bright-colored Dahlia gives the cue
    And maestro Wind responds,
He blows, he moans, and as he croons,
    They sway like magic wands

A POET'S DREAM Larry Empey

A poet writes of earth and sky
A tear, a smile, or just a sigh,
The morning dew upon a tree,
The things of life so fair to see.

Although a heartbreak always finds
A place within a poet's lines,
He writes them in solemnity,
This he feels, must always be.

And so he pours his thought in rhyme
Pours out his soul in every line,
He writes them down, both joy and grief
He phrases all to his belief.

And then I read these works by him,
Sorrow, joy, and foolish whim,
These wonders of his mind I see,
The things a poet knew could be.

MISERY   Ann Woodward

The moon is a shining disk suspended in a clean, clear sky.
        The trees and I,
                companions in misery,
                stretch empty arms imploring;
                my thoughts go soaring,
                hauntingly torturing me.
        My heart cries out
                for a time before
                when I knew no moon, no sun
                nor stars - save one
                I have no more.

CONTEMPLATIONS   Marilyn Kush

        Oh, how we love to watch the sky at night,
        With all its starry loveliness unveil.
        It makes us wonder why the clear moonlight
        Makes love, and hope, and dreams enthroned prevail.

        Scientists look upon our satellite,
        As a cold lump of rock, in which they fail
        To place faithfulness, not measured in height;
        They have but dreamed sadly of facts, so frail.

        So we turn our backs on this morose world
        And go soaring high above clouds of gloom,
        Where the future is bright and joy unfurled.

        We look not faithlessly down to our doom,
        But toward the moon, our thoughts upward hurled.
        That's why we love to watch the heavens bloom.

TOMORROW   Mary Lou Roos

        To those of us ambition fired
        Excuses merely make us tired.
        But find you few who seem to cling
        To promises for everything.

        In circumstances far removed
        With disappointments not soon soothed
        Brave pioneers are battling strife
        Forever threatening throughout life.

        Tomorrow holds the key of life
        For those who wish to conquer strife.
        But sad the disappointments brought
        To idlers' dreams and empty thoughts.

WITCHCRAFT   Su Schaible

Memory of last night's merriment,
Of roasted chestnuts by autumn moonlight,
And last year's hit tunes sung slightly off key -
A wisp of smoke along the trail reminds us
Of youthful pleasures.
Tonight the ghosts of yesteryear will dance
Grotesquely, as the acrid smoke of burning leaves
Floats on the wind, and leaping flames
Form witchlike patterns against the night,
While skeletons of leafless trees sway to and fro in tempo -
Autumn madness.

ABOUT DEATH   Kent Rylander

Before I breathe my final breath away,
And heavy lids wall out the light of day,
And weary limbs begin a long decay,
What will I say?

Will I, with hot and bitter tears begin
To curse and cry because I did not win
My fame with fiddle, brush or sword or pen
Like other men?

I'll humbly lift my lips to God and pray
For that strange thing called "life" I
            borrowed one day,
Ne'er to repay.
I'll pray that though I filled my life with sin,
And nasty rot my heart contained within,
I'll live again.

LONELINESS   Judith Caldow

Shadows softly creeping o'er the lake -
Cool, calm, glossy water,
Reflecting autumn in its depths -
One lone bird gliding far away -
Stillness ... awesome stillness.
Clear blue sky,
Fading into night's deep blackness -
Naked trees
Sharply outlined on the far horizon -
Peace . . . sad, still peace.
Green pines among red branches,
Soon red no longer -
No breeze, no noises heard -
Dark sky, still trees, deep water . . .
Loneliness.

INSPIRATION   Nancy Rolls

My soul is filled with the ecstasy of song;
It takes its winged flight to real, sublime,
Where music and life are together bound;
For now and for the rest of time.

With Schubert, Bach, and Brahms, together bound,
The music swells itself to greater depths than ere before;
And emotions, running through each bar and chord,
Touch the hearts of today and yore.

LOVE   Louise Strubel

My love is all the happiness I know,
And all the sorrow, too. It brings me all
My joy, and then as if a dreadful foe
Had stolen everything from me, I fall
So deeply into misery that no
Delivery seems possible until
You come, and I forget my woe
Till you are gone, or cannot hear my call.

To learn of beauty, one must become
Aware of gracelessness; and those who would
Know ecstasy, must first know pain. When done,
A fascination may be soon forgot,
But those who love, know love cannot.

SINCE YOU WENT AWAY   Helen Hester

As raindrops slowly fall
Outside my window pane,
Thoughts of you come tumbling
Back, to haunt my mind again.

As petals drop from the rosebush,
Gently fall onto my way,
I think of the dreams we shared
No other shared that day.

As I tread on the thorny briars,
My feet shall know no pain,
My only wishes are that
You will come home again.

I know there will come a time
When you, dear, shall return,
Then only you may see the tears
That on my cheeks shall burn.

MOODS   Judy Kirk

What do the branches of the trees
Whisper to each other in the night?
When skies are dark and gusty winds
Toss clouds about, hiding the moon from sight:
The whispers grow loud, and it seems the trees
Are angry with one another.
But on calm, cool nights such as tonight,
When you and I walk hand in hand
Beneath the stars, the trees
Harmonize with our mood
And whisper gently to each other.

POETRY FROM MY SOUL   Elsie Horvath

Poetry, rising and filling my soul,
Warming and sending a glow straight from my heart,
Forcing me to sound my happiness to the world
In the rhythmic flow of the lines, pouring
From the depths of my joyous heart, are unending.
Sweet sounds, caressing tones,
The lilting voice of the recitor
All are carried through the ether
To any welcome ear and heart
Sharing my happiness in such a way
Will create new thought to be expressed freely in
Poetry.

PEACE   Donna Bohnstedt

I hope that I may someday see
A world of peace with all men free,

A world whose selfishness is gone
Just like the dark right after dawn,

A world where men are all alike,
No racial problems to re-fight;

A world where wars are only found
In books so old they've been rebound,

A world where men are never bad,
Where peace, not war's the latest fad.

This parody was written by me
To show how peace on earth could be.

A LOVER'S PRAYER   Darleen Wilson

Oh Lord, please hear my prayer tonight. My love
Needs faith in Thee. He knows not of thy grace;
Nor of thy mighty strength. But, Lord, above,
Give him a deeper peace, a hiding place
Within his heart. Lord, let him see his life
As part of your great world - a world of trees,
A sphere of sky and clouds. For worldly strife
For him has dimmed the beauty of all these.
Oh, Lord, my love cannot go on for one
Who has no faith in thee. And so I pray
That he may see the light. Please let the sun,
The moon, the stars shine out to show the way,
For he does need thy strength each passing hour.
Oh, Lord, please show us all your mighty power.

CONQUEROR   Verna Hobbs

The dawn broke with a promise
To meet the challenge of the day,
To solve the problems and the heartaches
Accumulated on the way.

The sun set with a glow of glory,
Undefeated in its stay;
It had conquered all the coldness,
Left no problems still at bay.

LOVE   Sandra Miller

There's a time of life when everything
Is wonderfully pink,
And days turn golden through the clouds,
Without a warning wink.

The bad things seem to disappear,
And vanish out of sight,
To leave us marveling at the good,
That lingers day and night.

The milling mobs of race and creed,
With voices filled with hate,
Are lost somewhere in depths unknown,
To share a common fate.

But ones like us who live within,
A world with blue above
Have found that thing that wise men call,
The miracle of love.

BEAUTY IS EVERYWHERE   Marie Claire Ferrier

I am Beauty.
I am the expression in the blue eyes of a little boy
As he watches his smiling baby sister.
At other times I am the angry, whiteecapped Gulf
Exulting and splashing against the grey, weather-worn seawall.
Or again, I am the rolling, emerald-green highways of Alabama.

You will find me in the song of a mockingbird,
As well as in the whistling wind in old moss-covered trees.
On a sun-splashed June day,
Humming birds are attracted by my fragrance
In clover, or marigold or a deep-red rose.
In what you see, or hear, or touch, you will find me if you search for me.
I am Beauty.
And, I walk everywhere.

A LOOK AT LIFE   Dorrette McAdams

The other night I had a dream
While all was quiet and still -
I saw the millions trudging, climbing
Slowly up a hill.

The peasants, the tenants, the landlords
                              were there,
I saw the doctor, the Banker, the Parson,
The rich, the poor, the learned, the illiterate
They traveled, they struggled, all equal along.

It was then that I, the same mortal as these,
First thought of our life, of what it means.
I thought how I, somewhere in that throng,
Was destined to struggle and travel along.

EARLY SPRING   Rae Kabaker

When winter starts
Upon her leaving path
And grass becomes bright green
I long to sit beneath a tree
And await the fragrant scene.

So gentle
Are the blue and graying heavens
As if it were a rippling brook.
And Spring, with her cheery smile
Goes upon her way.

TIME'S WHIRLPOOL   Larry Freeman

Waves upon waves go doggedly on,
Fighting and conquering the men all along;
Dashing and breaking o'er continents wide,
Grasping at cities their wealth to hid.

Taking and hoarding men's lives from the world,
Men who tried conquering the force of the swirl;
Yet ages of culture lie 'neath the tide,
Waiting for men with horizons wide.

RAIN   Robert Mulligan

As I rise from sleep at morn,
From dreams that were so bright and sweet,
I sense the rain and feel forlorn,
For hopes and plans must meet defeat.

The sun and clouds won't play today;
The damp, dark sky will hide the sun,
The fleecy, fluffy beauties run away,
And moisture laden skies have fun.

My heart still throbs for yesterday,
The sky was bright and full of light,
But the sky today just seems to say,
"'Tis now my turn to have delight."

CITY   GeNel Baker

No stream here rushes, wild and free,
Gurgling, babbling merrily;
Instead, we send a child to play
In the city's gutters gray,
To sail his boats in sewers; but this,
This is the great metropolis.

There's one lone tree outside my sill,
Live and bravely green, but ill
Of this place as am I,
Sick of this place 'til I'll die
Of dirt and noise and crowds; but this,
This is the great metropolis.

And here the factories defy
The beauty of the very sky,
As they belch out their fumes and smoke,
Sunlight blot out, once-free air choke;
Ah, here it is man lives; for this,
This is the great metropolis.

DEATH   Nell Adams

Death is not for you to fear
His lips smile; his face is gentle as he draws near.
His eyes are soft and deep
To gaze in them is to sleep.
He kisses you and enfolds you in his wings of night
The flame of life dies
The soul rises in flight,
At the closing of the eyes
Thro' black space glowing with fairy stars
The stir of his sable pinions
Is as music of muted violins.

THE ASS SPEAKS   Robert M. Longsworth, Jr.

Look at my ears, how long are they,
How stubborn I am, or so men say,
How short and stout, this ugly beast,
My hay and grain is my only feast.

And man - he laughs when he looks at me,
But - he doesn't see what he ought to see.
For man wasn't there when the Child was born;
But I saw His birth, and then at morn
Some shepherds - then some wise men came,
And t h e y said that He was a child of fame.

Yes, lowly am I, and I toil in the fields;
And I can but reap of mankind's yields;
Yet man may scorn, and laugh at me,
But I have felt glory, greater than he.

HAPPINESS   Molli Morris

I love
But alas
So in vain
The meadow, the flower,
The sunset so rare.

I love
But alas
Not in vain
For it is happiness
They have to spare.

R. I. P.   Mary Derengowski

The trees stand stark against the sky,
    Too desolate to weep.
And with the doleful north wind merge
The mournful accents of a dirge
    For Autumn, in death's sleep.

Dark storm clouds gather in the sky.
    The mourners whisper low,
While countless snowflakes, drifting down,
Lay Autumn gently underground,
    Wrapped in a shroud of snow.

CAVATINA   Sue Conover

Life is but one sweet overture
Of music
In God's great masterpiece,
A prelude to the great symphony
Of the eternal spheres.

Play each bar gently -
Its full beauty to reflect;
Each living thing imparts
Its note
To the harmonious Whole.

MUSIC AND FLOWERS   Linda Phillips

Harmony, Music and Flowers,
    Beautiful, arts of man and nature.
Notes of exquisite, blending, composure
Ring and resound throughout the bowers,
    Music and flowers.

Soft and lilting, like "Babies Breath,"
    Striking and crescending as "Zinnias,"
Quaint as "Pansies," Music and Flowers,
Painting hues in forest bowers,
    These together, Music and flowers.

Blending, painting, singing, bringing,
    Lovely hues throughout this sphere.
These two we acknowledge here
    Music, man's art, and nature's flowers.

BEAUTY   Harold Smith

I met beauty on a crowded street
Between the patter of hurrying feet
I met it in the winter, there was cold and sleet
But I met it best on a crowded street
I met it in the springtime, the birds chirped with glee
I also foud it out on the open sea
But I met beauty best, on the crowded street.

SPACE   Sandra Kay Brown

Space extends to Infinity,
Stretching beyond Eternity,
Dark and void, a great nothingness -
And what begins where space evaporates,
No one can tell.

FIRE   Bill O'Quin

Crackle, crackle, pop!
Ignis, always hop!

Ancient Rome and Troy
Felt your fingers cloy;
New Chicago grew,
Then was burned by you.

Crackle, crackle, pop
Ignis, never stop!

Spring, sprang, sprung
Leaps your eager tongue,
Burning all in view
Till at last you're through.

Crackle, crackle, pop
Ignis, always hop!

Sol gave you your life
Vesta kept you rife;
Like a holy lyre
Sing your song, O fire!

Crackle, crackle, pop
Ignis, never stop!

Tear, tore, torn
Till you are reborn;
Fan yourself a lot
Keep your flame red-hot.

Crackle, crackle, pop!
Ignis, always hop!

FOREST CITY   Marilyn Chappell

A forest city - looming above and on all sides.
Animals are people, each on his mission
The strong trampling on the weak to attain their goals.
Paths are streets,
Trees are buildings piercing the clouds.

A forest city - looming above and on all sides,
The holes in the ground are houses
Wherein people of all nations may dwell.
Grass is a carpet,
Clearings are post offices where news is passed.

ASHES   Bill Donovan

Ashes hot, ashes cold,
Ashes in the grave - many years old.

This matter once so warm and comforted
    in the womb secure and all curled up
Then set loose to drift aimlessly as
    a pinball between pockets,
Now and then attracted, then repelled
But finally put to rest by inertia -
    unrelenting law.
Or, as these, again, very hot
And maybe scattered o'er sea
Or poured into an urn, very symmetrically
    made to receive the ashes -

But at the last these must,
Necessarily must, be cold.

WILD DUCKS   Larry K. Vaughn

High over the marshes formations passed
On strokes of power
Winging the way south.
I watched motionless but no course diverted
Toward my ready gun,
For I was the subject of many eyes,
They the subject of two.

In life it appears the same to me.
With a daily mission the multitudes pass,
Each mind unknown to others'
Inspiring course of thought.
My actions, held in the eyes of others
Are given many different values,
Although I judge them acceptable.

A SONG IN MY HEART   Barbara Goralnik

Someone told me I wouldn't succeed,
Someone said I was wrong.
But to their warnings I paid no heed,
And now in my heart there's a song.

I was doomed for failure said those with no trust,
And by this phrase I was haunted.
But I knew that my job was an absolute must,
My courage couldn't be daunted.

For though my life's span has been short
This important lesson I've learned -
That to end up with a song in one's heart
Is not so easily earned.

THE GOLDEN STRAIN   Nancy Magnusson

A strain of music,
So soft and sweet,
With strong emotion
And warmth so deep
Came floating in
And caught my ear.

It sang of wind,
And rain and storm,
Of slumbering,
And young ones born,
And filled my heart
With thoughts so clear.

I'm glad that strain, so soft and clear,
Came floating in and caught my ear.

THE RAINBOW   Jerry Brinker

A flashing gleam of light,
    a perfect, streamlined form,
    a splash, then silence;
    a raindrop has come home.
First high in the clouds
    then falling, falling,
    faster, faster,
    until, finally it dashes
    vainly;
    against the sturdy earth ...
Will mankind overlook
    the lesson of the raindrop?

DESTINY   Margaret A. Gruner

With the desperateness of our
youth, purged of its gaiety
We are waiting to die.

And in the cool of the brook,
underwater leaves sway lazily
as relentless time marches on.

We do not mind the dying, God, but
our time is brittle now. Before we go,
give us the reason why.

A THANKSGIVING THOUGHT   Nancy Malaun

Not for the boundless wealth of lands,
          The turbulent ocean's mighty span,
          Our virgin forests, our desert sands.

Not for the sky of celestial blue,
          The sunset with its amber hue,
          Our mighty mountains proud and true.

Not for the brooks that gaily sing,
          The gentle breezes that hint of spring,
          Our rains that give life to thirsty things.

Not for these things do we humbly say,
          Thank You, God, on Thanksgiving day.

Not for these do we hail this day serene,
          But for the love that in them is seen.

WASHED WINDOWS   Margaret Kinnicutt

Green light lifts young leaves.
Wild birds hunt and sing.
Cool water rises, meets steady rocks.
New cars ride smooth roads -
And so the young man looks.

Crisp wood burns in fall fires.
Damp winds blow tired flocks south.
Ice cuts and covers land.
Lone cars ride ridged frozen clay -
And so the old man sees.

THE SEASHORE - PORTLAND, MAINE   Dudley F. Uphoff, Jr.

I went all the way to the sea one day and saw
Flatness and wetness stretching away from me --
The flat land and the flat sea - straight lines -
Monotony. It trifled not
        With the sky.

The clouds, in all their sweeping swirls -
In all their little spots, touched tenderly
The earth in vaporous humility.
The horizon line was damp. I watched birds
        Drifting over me.

The gulls, the little dots of gulls,
Grew bigger and brighter as they came to me
From out of the sky where they lived.
They soared above calling shrill,
        Hideous sounds.

MY CATHEDRAL   Ann Mackert

Rib vaulted are the branches of my trees,
    Whose spires grope ever for a distant heaven.

Rose windowed is the surface of my stream,
    Whose happy music is my song of praise.

My nave, grass tufted, boasts a feathered choir
    And flute-toned organ, mellow in the wind.

'Neath cloudy arches darts my furry host
    Unaware of this, my green cathedral.

THE SUMMIT   Susan Bell

Love is like a mountain
Reaching to the sky,
And the wind upon it
Like a lover's sigh,

But a mountain's heart is granite,
And a lover's heart is flesh;
Yet love is like a mountain,
Ever-lasting, ever fresh.

Yes, love is like a mountain,
Like its summit pure and white;
And those who reach that summit
Reach the soul's most peaceful height.

PRIDE'S CASTLE　　　　　Peggy Dowdy

They say
　　That pride has a castle
That can hold
　　Millions of dreams.

Then why
　　If pride has a castle,
Can one little tear
　　Tear down its dreams,
And send them floating in a stream
　　Of tears from a lover's eyes?

IVORIES　　Sarah Berman

Eighty-eight barriers of ivory forever　　shut
　　　　to the nescient.
You who the password　　　　　　　　　know
　　　　can enter, alone.
Those who read the code can　　　　　　make
　　　　the fortress tumble.
To the beat of the flat drums they　　　　fall
　　　　in the west.
The keys in the east　　　　　　　　　　peal
　　　　in mourning.

Black-capped elves on strings　　　　　fast
　　　　know.

MEMORY　　　　Faith Pleasants

Why is it that in the quiet of the night
When all the earth and heaven is asleep
I wake, remember, then try to fight
My haunting memory.

The memory of nights long gone
Nights when we exchanged kisses
Endearing embraces, and whispered words of
　　　　　　　　　　　　　　　love
All in a world of silver and black velvet
Made radiant by our love
This I see now, in
My Haunting Memory.

Now, all the bliss is past.
Nothing remains but the bitter tears
and the rendering heartbreak.
Yet one more thing will last
My Haunting Memory.

SWIFT PASSING   Charles Stegmeier

Sitting there beside the endless night
I watch the vast expanse of space and darkness
Engulfing all save fleeting gleams of light
That vainly try to keep alive day's furnace.

The futile houses sprinkled on the plain
Are swallowed up by night's pervading fog
Leaving here and there a gleaming pane -
The only critic of night's monologue.

A GIFT OF NATURE   Mary Margaret VanHoose

A rose in bloom is a flow'r of perfection,
All beauty is shown in its reflection;
Mother Nature placed it here,
For us to cherish and hold dear.

This elegant flower in majesty sways,
It nods its head as it watches life's ways;
Undaunted in spirit by all its surroundings,
To all behold it, gives beauty abounding.

Red or yellow, pink or white,
To all mankind a pleasing sight;
Like human life, roses die, too,
But spring brings them back with life anew.

THE SEARCH   Sally Ann Rosenheimer

The caravan moves slowly on,
The camel bells ring 'cross the sand,
As I with weary feet do tread
The Golden Road to Samarkand.

My head this night no pillow finds,
My limbs no comfort feel,
And I have sorrows of the world
That I dare not reveal.

My rose of life has withered now,
Its petals brown and fall,
And I must seek a better life
Along a pillared hall.

So I forever on do go,
My hours are but a lonely span,
Following the only hope I have
The Golden Road to Samarkand.

REMINDERS   Franziska Neumann

Every existing thing is a spectre of something to someone
A record of a dream, an inane desire;
          a feeling that was never spent.
On a leaf dotted with glimmering
        specks of dewdrops,
          reflecting their radiance in the climbing sun,
An artist can envision a scene
         upon his empty canvas, his masterpiece fulfilled.
Silver birds crossing the sky,
        like winge'd Mercury stir up
Old flames and dreams of far away
         as though their presence were but seconds before.
Crystal goblets tapped together
        as casually while dining,
Re-echo as a sonata or prelude
        to the soul whose Ellisium
        is filled with music.
An empty reverie is no haven,
        but who can flee a moment
Recaptured by a memory?

SILVER RAIN   Doris Ruth Hohlfeld

It rained one summer afternoon,
A silver rain and over soon.
Then sidewalks, washed with showery
        tears,
Became a path of patchwork mirrors,
Reflecting back in torn-up parts,
Green leaves, grey skies, and broken
        hearts.

A LIGHT   Marjorie Hillsman

In the night, a light
Brightened my weary way,
In the night that light
Guided me until day.

It beckoned me,
It softly gave me cheer,
Shone upon my footsteps
Until my path was clear.

In my life His love
Brightens the way for me
Guiding me through life
On toward eternity.

THE HUNTED   Marilyn Berner

Pause not, oh deer! pause not!
Pause not to gaze upon the silent trees,
Reaching toward Heaven, yet standing like sentinels.
Pause not to glance upon the chill, cold brook,
Tumbling over rocks, and bubbling out its joy of life.
Pause not to listen to the icy blasts of the December wind.
Pause not to survey from a hilltop the kingdom that is yours,
Or the silver, sparkling white of the snow.
Pause not, for the hunter pauses not to gaze
Upon this beauteous scene which God has given the winter.

Race on, oh thing of beauty! race on!
Race on for your freedom, for your life, race on.
Knowest thou where bound for,
Knowest thou whether thou shalt lie stiff and cold
On the frozen ground,
Or whether thy limbs will be spared to flee another year?
With thy timid, limpid, liquid eyes, and all thy beauty,
Knowest thou why the hunter hunts thee,
Why he would rather see thee lifeless upon the ground,
Rather than gaze upon thee gliding gracefully over streams
                    unbounded?
Nor do I know what joy he finds in destroying beauty.

TOGETHER FOR ETERNITY   Jeanne McKibben

Do you remember a day long ago
    When time seemed to stand so still?
Just you and I, alone at twilight,
    Moving about at His own will.

I shall never forget that memory
    And I hope 'twill remain with you, too,
For you are the sand, and I am the sea,
    Together for eternity.

TO A PIECE OF CHALK   Sonny Ohlenbusch

Little chalk upon the shelf
Why keep all your knowledge to yourself?
When I don't know the answer true,
Can't you supply a hint or two?
You're very smart in Teacher's hand,
With me you take the opposite stand.
I try to be nice and kind to you;
Yet you do things I wouldn't do,
Like, on the board draw pictures and verses
That put me at the principal's mercies.
Shame on you, you little white stick.
Pull something for me beside a trick.

NO RETURNING   Jackye McLean

Things move slowly, very slowly, down the gutter ...
Into a deep black pit from which there is no turning back ...
A candy bar wrapper, thrown carelessly there by some child,
Eager to make the 2:00 matinee -
A cigarette butt, with its end crushed to a pulp ...
As if its owner, with some problem on his mind, expected to find
The answer in the smoke and became angry when he did not -
The picture - drawn so carefully by the first grader -
Whose heart was broken when his mother laughed -
The prescription, written by such a skilled, rich hand -
Thrown into the muddy water by the dirt farmer ...
Whose children will suffer because of the lack of that substance
Known as money ...
And so life goes by - in many and varied patterns -
And the swish of the objects makes a sound, all its own, like music -
Music signifying death and a journey from which there is no return ...

SOMERSAULT   Shirley Elaine Dryden

First I stand upon my head,
In the field of pink and white clover.
The world about is upside down
Until I roll halfway over.

Then I stand upon my feet,
As proud and glad as I can be,
To find that roof tops really do
Hold up the chimneys that I see.

NATURE   Ramona Bailey

Speak fast, you mighty villain,
You robber of the trees,
Who in the autumn steal away
The falling autumn leaves

You cause the winter snow to fall
Leave land so white and bleak
You freeze the great wide rivers
And all the ponds and creeks

So sparkle, all ye flakes of snow,
Ye bands of frozen glass
For another year is all but here
And I fear you will not last.

EDUCATION   Bobby Makemson

A reputable scholar once said,
For every brilliant man that makes his mark,
Ten thousand worthy intellects are dead,
Ten thousand virtuous minds lie in the dark.
We know through sad experience of our own,
Through worthy words that famous men have said,
That many wasting geniuses have failed,
While many zealous fools have forged ahead.
We are but puppets governed by one great,
And mighty prophesier of our day,
We cannot change the passage of our fate,
But education helps to pave the say.
So fix your course to meet that far-off star,
And though the present day may not be fair,
The destination is not really far,
And education is your ticket there.

SEARCHING   Gloria Tinto

I've been searching!
Searching for the love that offsets the hatred,
Searching for the joy that banishes the gloom,
Searching for the light that replaces the darkness.
Yes, I've been searching.

I went searching.
I thought I had found the love;
I was sure I had found the joy;
I didn't think I'd ever see the darkness again,
But that changed somehow;
I am still searching.

I shall keep searching;
I might find the love again;
I'm almost certain to find the joy;
I want to find the light to replace darkness;
The road seems so long -
But I shall keep on searching.

IT'S ONLY DARK   Jerry Raun

It's only dark,
Deep dark,
Cool, soothing dark -
I love the dark.
It folds me in its arms.
It calms my fears and heals my scars.
It's only sleep,
Sweet sleep,
Cool, soothing sleep -

NATURE'S CARPET   Bob Hatcher

The leaves float down to earth again this fall
To make a rug for God's own vast domain.
His weaver was not of this earthly life,
For work like this must come from far beyond.
The color in this work of art must be
From some great artist's tubes of heavenly hues.
So when you walk upon this heavenly work,
Remember that God's walking there with you.

DAYDREAM   Moira Burk

I lie here
Gazing at the sky,
Not thinking,
Just musing,
Feeling the warmth of the summer afternoon;
Smelling the sweet crushed grass
Beneath my body;
Hearing the lazy, busy hum of the bees
Sampling each clover blossom;
Wondering if that bit of
Very white, very fluffy cloud
Is the tail of a baby rabbit
Gone to heaven . . .

FALLEN SPIRITS   Alton C. Smith

The golden castles that I built
   Have vanished from my sight;
The Diamond fields that glittered so
   Have vanished like the night.

The dreams I knew have tumbled
   In heaps upon the ground;
My future now is dark and drear
   With trouble all around.

The smile is gone from on my lips
   My face is set and grim;
I guess I'll never smile again
   The chances are so slim.

Oh, just one word of comfort
   To help me on my way;
For I must tread a dreary path
   In perilous life each day.

NIGHT   Alice Michalaros

How low the moon hangs from its place in the sky,
Like a pendant strung by stars on a silver chain of moonbeams.
Beauty pallid from the lamp of night shines brightly
Upon an undeserving world.

From the sphere of golden yellow, little moonbeams dance
Upon waters and streams and in the eyes of lovers.

WHEN   Mary Greve

When has pain e'er brought relief,
Or conflict formed a band?
When has wealth brought happiness,
Or scowls a friendly hand?

When has greed true comfort made,
Or quarrels trouble cease?
When has darkness given light,
Or war a living peace?

PORTRAIT OF A POET AS A YOUNG MAN
                    John E. Lankford
School boy,
Dreamer of high dreams
philosophy for breakfast
politics for lunch
poetry for supper
theology for late evening snacks
and all day Sunday.

Brow heated by the
scorching winds of
reform . . . .
and cooled by the
soothing caresses of science . . .
He sits alone,
and fathoms the Universe
with pad and pencil.
A modern Omar . . .

His printed verse
is not his best.
The best is shared
between the poet and God
and only printed on his heart.

DREAMS   Carol Weast

Dreams are made of stardust;
Enchanting you with their beauty,
Beauty that enthralls you,
Holding you captive in its web.
Just a little web so silken
Silky strands, soft and strong,
Their strength binding you tightly,
Holding you captive until dawn.

WORKBENCH   Francis V. McBride

With a strong Frame formed by Home and School,
With Knowledge for my surest Tool,
With the Glue of Persistence, never letting go,
With Patience when the work is slow;
With nails of the hard metal of Truth,
With Integrity's Square to make the whole foolproof,
And with Courage to trace my own design
The Workbench I build is this Life of mine.

TWILIGHT   John Dardess

When the eve-tide's sultry shadows
Separate the meadow from the wood-land
And the sparrow's song is carried
From the brooklet to the farmhouse
And the splendor of the sunset
Like one thousand knights in armor
Like one thousand swords of fire
Reflects its light upon the deep-lake
Slowly creep the somber shadows
From the mountains to the wood-land.
In the stillest part of evening
I sit upon the boulder
And listen to the woodland noises
Softly creeping from the forest.
Then when the long black shadows cover
All the wood-land and the meadow
Comes the thrush's sweet night-vesper
And I leave the big-rock in the pasture
For the dusk has gone, and the nightfall
Covers all from hill to woodland.

HOSPICE   Ethel Marcinek

The string of lights in the distance
Means a town is not far away.
Lights in the houses are burning;
Food, clothing and shelter
Await us.

The myriad of stars in the sky
Means God is not far away.
Lights in His heavenly home are gleaming;
Love, peace, and His blessing
Await us.

GREATEST OF ALL   David Fellmeth

I gazed upon a child's face
        and saw the innocence of youth.
I looked upon a white-capped mountain
        standing majestic and tall,
And after each, I thought
        it was the greatest vision of all.

I saw a flowing mountain stream
        surrounded by leafless trees in the fall
And to myself I thought,
        "This is the greatest vision of all."

But then, one day, I looked on Christ's Cross
        It - that brought salvation to us all,
And I knew that at last I had found
        The greatest vision of them all.

RETURN OF THE PRAIRIE WANDERERS
                    Patricia Miner

Moss agate stone
And buffalo bone
Dry and porous
We put before us.

Indian arrow tip,
Antelope marrow bit,
Blossom of grass,
Quartz clear as glass.

This morning we wandered
Beyond the dry river,
And this we have gathered
As memory for ever.

MOMENT   Joy Annah Brown

Time holds a bubble in his hand,
Encasing a single golden moment.
And clocks like sentinels stand by
Trying to pierce it with their pricking, punching hands.

I'll smash those sentry clocks
And snatch my bubble from Time's grasp,
To hold it up, lift it high ...
Sheltered - in a memory.

CATHEDRAL IN MY HEART   Margaret Jones

There is a great cathedral in my heart ...
Not like those of the Ages,
Not of the stone and mortar
Which raised pulseless hands to the sky,
Not of the toil of Man
And his generations.

Centuries of Time
Have not scaled the walls and loosed the moorings.
Time has been but one grain of sand
Through the interminable glass
Upon this fortress of solidity.

I have entreated no man to live his span
To renew the labors of his ancestry.
I am the mason with torn hands.
It is my sacred structure ...
A gift of Me to Mine.
Crumbling? .... yes.
But lo! I have a great cathedral in my heart,
And there, amidst the ruins,
I will meditate.

A BOUNTY   Wilkes Berry

The world demands; her sons reply,
And yield the price, however high.
The trees are felled, earth's treasures reached;
The wastelands tamed, the rivers leashed.
And man must too a bounty pay
To feed his world in every way,
With noblest thought and finest bread.
This must he do until he's dead.

234

SUCCESS STILL Marthajane Gregory

I cut new stars
From silvered fragments
Of my broken dreams
To fling them at the moon
Now everyday that passes
A fraction of my heart returns in
Silver snowflakes, silver rain, or
Silver beams escaping from the sky.

SNOW Dorothy Downs

God laid upon this naked earth
    an altar cloth of purest white;
Then, while the world around Him slept,
    He prayed there in the night.

The morning sun, in haste to reign,
    removed the cloth from this terrain,
Leaving the country bare again.

BEAUTY OF POETRY Mary Lee Abba

A poet amasses
    Sparkling diamonds in a raindrop;
Great shining emeralds
    On the crown of the treetop.

Nymph-like beauty
    In a blade of wavering grass,
Where cunning little
    Elves around it pass.

Twinkling stars scamper
    Through the misty sky;
As the moon gazes down
    He winks his eye.

With capricious imagination
    And delicate thought,
A new ditty or poem
    Into the world will be brought.

EVENING   Barbara Kirkman

I love the gentleness that evening brings
The silver pencil of moonlight
Scribbles its autograph
On these solemn hills
And the first stars
Smile their sleepy hellos.
A kind of peacefulness
Comes over you,
And all the cares of the day
Are gathered up
Like stray lambs
And l ed into the fold of night.

SPEECH   Michael Smith

O, why so harsh do you crack,
and bite into flesh so deep.
In ferocious rage you smack,
deepening wounds so that out of me
        seeps
    the life of me.
From what contorted mind was the idea
      expounded,
    that for misery you were intended.
The cruelties of men into you were
      blended,
So that when cruelty was offended,
    You took the life of me.

LINCOLN   Diane Elizabeth Shaver

Cold sorrow's sting, not victory's call,
A summons in life's empty hall,
Where echoes from a frightening dark
Compress the last warm golden spark
That frees man's soul of sorrow's pain.
And Lincoln? Alas! Stung but again.
Then grew he strong from loathsome test
And stumbled not as have the rest.
But onward strode through greater strife
To learn from God true love of life.
So sublime a lesson taught
By one who climbs and falters not,
A path so narrow, crooked and worn
Beaten down by jeers and scorn.
The deafened ear and numbered mind
Made stumblers partners with the blind.

TWILIGHT   Joyce Zimmer

The twilight . . . .
A bending mist of dust
Of light diffused to form . . .
These lovely hours between light and dark
And dark and light
When things not clear but softly blurred
Will shimmer, surprise, and diminish; lured
By the rest and peace of night,
By the activity and day of light.

ATOMIC CHIVALRY   Lawrence Sperry, Jr.

In this era - new, atomic,
Only bums feel manners comic,
Those whose clothes do not need patches,
But whose glaring habits do.

Hatred marks their iron features,
Since they are such left-out creatures.
Still, their mode of living matches
Daily conduct at the zoo.

In an era - armor plated,
Courtesy was not outdated.
Knights in fights, though sore with scratches,
Were polite to all they slew.

When your mirror shows reflections
Of bad habits, make corrections
Because of you let it be said
That chivalry is never dead.

THE FROWNING CLIFF   Shirley Porter

The sea has a laugh,
And the cliff has a frown;
For the laugh of the sea
Is wearing him down.

Lipping and lapping,
Frown as he may
The laughing sea
Will eat him away.

Knees and body,
And tawny head,
He will smile at last
On a Golden Bed.

MY UTTERMOST DESIRE   Jimmie Campbell

I'd like to be a poet, who gives so much to all
A poet who would think each day and write of nature's call
A poet who is familiar with the swaying of the trees
And one who understands and knows why they shed their leaves.

I desire to have a poet's mind and all that comes within
A gentle heart, a loving mind and powers to comprehend,
If all the essential qualities were in my power to give,
I'd make this earth a greater spot and a better place to live.

I SAW THREE STRAY GEESE FLY   Elmer Lee Sandusky

I saw three stray geese fly.
Silently they went by.
Lost from the flock they were.
Southward their wings did whir.
Circling water, shirking
Danger, they went searching.
Onward, northward, they flew.
Gustly the north wind blew.
One led, two did follow.
They did distance swallow.

AH! IT'S SPRING   Grace Tinebra

Someone laughed and kissed my face
She made me feel anew
Someone led me by the hand
To show me beauty's view

Balmy breezes tease my hair
Flowers bow, dressed in style
Birds hold daily symphonies
My breath is gone awhile

Aqua sky with powder puffs
Emerald grass like straw
Lost in wonderland's delight
A soul could ask no more

Quickly though she fluttered off
It made my heart to yearn
In my hair's her daffodil
With news that she'd return

MY SOUL   Patricia Weber

I have been very busy;
My soul and I have been communicating,
And from my soul I draw forth answers
To the perplexing problems of the day.

My soul is a perplexing problem in itself;
To be a complete person, I must get to know my soul.
It is as elusive as a will o' the wisp.
When I catch it I must keep it.

WORDS   Ellen Payton

Mix them together,
Tear them apart,
Any way you put them,
They go to your heart.

Sometimes they're lovely,
Sometimes they're mean,
Some ways you say them
They have horrible stings.

Use them with care
So they won't hurt.
Love them, cherish them
For they ... are words.

I DO LOVE A CHRISTMAS TREE
Doris N. McNitt

There was a time, not long ago,
When, happy as could be,
A little fellow murmured low,
"I do love a Christmas Tree."

How many other youngsters small,
While perched on Daddy's knee,
Have said about that tree so tall,
"I do love a Christmas Tree."

It seems to be the usual thing
From mountains to the sea,
For children all to gleefully sing,
"I do love a Christmas Tree."

It isn't much for us to do
And what a joy to see
The shining eyes of children, who
"Do love a Christmas Tree."

SCULPTURE   Ruby Waltemath

So old, and yet so young, the desert sands!
So alabaster pure that angels' hands
Would leave no imprint in the silken drifts.
So restless! Zephrus' fingers mold his gifts
Of sculptured beauty.

THE CAVES   Margaret Yarina

Along the earth's uneven crust
A million half-hid caverns thrust
Their yawning faces through the dust
            Like gaping eyes.
Their walls are hung with mosses green
While on all sides great boulders lean
Their formless shoulders on the scene
            Like countless spies.

From far below, no voices sound
No human heartbeats pulse or pound
No glint of life, no love is found,
            No trace of mirth.
These orbs shall never cease to stare
Upon the world and all that's there
Eternally standing, bleak and bare
            Like windows of the inner earth.

O GOD   Eugene Cramer

(the dream)
            Sunshine and rain,
            Flowers and grain,
            Beautiful, Glorious,
            Grand and Almighty.

(the realization)
            Hearts burst in twain,
            Blood on the plain,
            Horrible, terrible,
            Death and destruction.
(the cure)
            Out of this sight,
            There came a light,
            Shining bright, Shining long,
            Into the night.

            God save the world,
            Let there be peace,
            Oh God.

THE DAY   Maryann Porter

The sun is shining brightly
And there is warmth in the blue sky
The children are skipping lightly,
Thru the fields of golden rye.

The trees and flowers are in their glory
And the grass is green as can be,
But if it rained, we would be sorry,
As the beautiful day would end for me.

COCKY LITTLE SPARROW   May Eula Routt

Cocky little sparrow,
What makes you so bright.
You sing and fly and sing some more
And then you sleep all night.

Cocky little sparrow
Cat chased you up a tree,
But when you got upon a limb
You chirped and winked at me.

MAJESTIC JOURNEY   Esther McCracken

I saw a fairy kingdom in
    The sky the other night,
With dragons, queens, and hunters,
    What a beautiful sight!

I saw a lovely field of white
    With stars as flow'rs of May
Form an arch across the sky,
    'Twas the Great White Milky Way.

I saw Orion the hunter
    The Dog Star, just close by,
Come bowing to Cassiopeia,
    Lovely queen of the sky.

The Great Bear drank from the Dipper
    The Little Bear by her side,
And soon the whole sky was sleeping
    O'er the peaceful countryside.

SOLITUDE   Roberta White

In the midst
Of the hot and desolate desert
Where the rolling dunes
Stretch out for miles on end,
Stands a lonely, gnarled old tree,
Dark against
The scorched white sands.

JUST PRETEND   Margaret Dellis

Let's just pretend there is no sorrow,
    Just pretend there are no trials.
That life is just a gay tomorrow -
    Never any cares along those long, long miles.

Just pretend that loss is profit,
    Just pretend that failure's gain.
That there are no tearful moments
    When the world seems full of rain.

And when you just pretend these things,
    No matter who you are;
You'll find you feel much better now,
    Like wishing on a star.

Every trial will seem a blessing,
    Every foe will feel a friend.
And that muddy road - a highway,
    If you will just pretend.

THE LILY OF THE VALLEY   Mary Lee Gill

        As I stood on the hillside
One morning in May,
I saw a white lily,
So little, so gay.
        A dainty white blossom
Nodding its head,
As the soft breeze of Springtime
Swept 'round its small bed.
        With its delicate perfume
It sent praises to God;
'Twas reaching toward Heaven
With each little nod.
        I thought, as I stood there,
How true it must be,
He who cares for the lilies
Surely careth for me.

242

THE SEA   Tonia Marett

Have you ever played upon its shore
And run upon its sandy beach?
Or seen the gulls dart to and fro
In the azure sky - ' way out of reach?

Have you ever heard its monstrous roar
As it beats upon the whitened sands?
Have you ever gathered the coral shells
And wished you might have two more hands?

THE SKY   Howard Nihei

The never ending skies above
Challenge men to reach the top
So men studied, planned and tried;
But will they ever reach so far
To meet the challenge of the sky?

Leonardo Da Vinci and the Wright brothers,
Charles Lindbergh, and many others
Did their share to conquer the sky.
Since their days men have advanced further
To fly faster and higher in the sky.

In a sense, today, we've conquered the sky.
We have learned much of her tempers, her storms,
The gales and hurricanes which she unleashes.
But in the future we'll learn more of her
To beat the challenge of the sky.

GOLDEN SEAS   Gail Belaief

Golden Seas
Great fields
Of wheat that sway
In breezes, slow at first
And then with sudden vigor - that
Is life.

Dormant Beauty
The tall,
Straight columns stand
Alone, remaining from
An age of beauty, long ago
Forgot.

MAGIC   Margo Wiley

Perhaps there is no magic in this world,
But a dewdrop on a spring rose,
An Indian paintbrush in its splendor,
The fall leaves in all their bright colors,
And the happiness of Christmas.
Yet surely these things are the magic of God.

COLD, NORTH WIND   Betty Broerman

Blowing, blowing, the cold winds go,
Freezing the streams so they cannot flow,
Biting our cheeks till they're aglow,
Bringing with them the cold, white snow.
Stinging our eyes till they are bright,
Blotting the scenes from out our sight,
Swirling the snow with all thy might,
Dark'ning our view as though it's night.
Guide me, lead me, on the right path,
Spare me all thy hideous wrath.
Blowing onward ever so free,
Seeking out thy destiny.

THE FLIGHT   Virginia Hughes

Two hands have I to do the things
We humans must do from dawn till night,
While fowl of air are blessed with wings
To assist them in celestial flight.

I, poor mortal, must be content
To knead the bread and wield the pen,
As my feathered friends climb the height,
To heaven's clear and crystal light.

Ah, could I but wing through space
At brother eagles' breathless pace,
Gladly would I forsake these hands
To hover above all worldly lands.

But how shall I e'er ascend
Near the angels, away from men?
Lest I in some mystic way
Free my soul from earthen clay.

Two hands have I to do all things
In a loving, generous way
That they may gain for me my wings
To fly to Heaven's height one day.

DO NOT REACH FOR THE MOON   Lois Ralston

Do not reach for the moon to hold in your hands,
Or to light up your life and show you the right path.

Do not dream of the moon in a world of real people,
In the midst of reality and real relationships.

Do not wish by the moon for a lover or a song,
There is no place in this world of real things for a dreamer,
And no time to waste as a parasite on the moon.

TWILIGHT REVERIE   Pat Smith

Leaves drift slowly down, to nestle
Lightly on the almost frozen ground.
Bare branches are outlined in the failing light,
Patiently awaiting the inevitable night.
The mocking bird sings its last song,
A prelude to the night's long
Symphony of the dark's particular sounds
Started when Twilight makes her rounds.

The wind comes up, and it is cool
As it rustles the trees and ripples the pool,
Stars twinkle in the velvet sky,
And the moon looks down as the clouds brush by.
Looking down on the breathtaking scene,
One could imagine it was a giant screen,
Where a million dramas are played in the night,
Only to vanish with the coming light.

JASBO'S CELLAR   Marcia Jones

A Dixieland trumpet speaks loud and proud
While the tapping feet and the throbbing beat
Of drums, which are echoing primitive man
          Roll sensuously.

The saxaphone talks smooth and cool,
Sobs and pleads with a reedy-toned soul,
To a smoke-filled room of dark and deaf
          Humanity.

Half-shut eyes on a glistening face,
Creatures burning their lives of jive
As sacrifice, to the off-beat rhythm
          Of ecstasy.

CHANGE OF MOOD   Mary Jo Wilbur

Look hard into the ocean,
Watch the different currents plunging, clashing,
Finally roaring into submission on the white sands
Of the shore,
Laying its secrets open for the wise to see.
It is a lover,
Poised on the surface,
Yet filled with turbulent currents
Shifting and swirling underneath.
It is a child,
Laughing with the wind,
Tossing its blue robes of sea into the air,
Slapping the frolicsome porpoise on his head
With flashing fingers of foam.
It is the executioner,
Waiting with lustful foresight for the hard-pressed serviceman,
Angry with revengeful wrath
If a single soul escapes her sailors grave.
It is nature,
Sweeping her shores with foam,
Try, in a small way, to clean her part of a dirty, tired world.

MY WISH   Patricia J. Kennedy

I wish I could dream of a wonderful sight,
A dream I could live far into the night;
A dream of a trip to a far distant land,
Where breezes blow 'cross the sun-warmed sand;
Where the sea is as blue as the overhead sky,
And the palm trees sway to a melodious sigh;
Where the nights are cool and the stars are bright,
And the moon shines down with a phantom light;
Where colorful flowers bloom through the year,
Where no one would know the meaning of fear;
A paradise like this only touched by the sun,
Where I could go when my day is done.

AN INVITATION, NO REGRET!
          Sally Tupper Sherman Anderson

Swift and strong her web she wove
A small spider's silken home,
Embroidered with care
This net she would share
With curious ones who seek and roam.
This silver - spun lacey net
Hung with an invitation, no regret!

DAWN   Nanette Andersen

In wonder I have witnessed life's odd play,
The prelude - darkness, the act was - day.

        I saw a seagull hush the morning sea
        And then a sun rose high - majestically.
        A somber breeze embraced the ocean waves
        And echoed, lonely, in the haunted caves.
        The valleys stirred in irritated sleep
        And then as if unworthy - fed their sheep.
        The aging mountains stretched, then yawned,
        And suddenly the world gave birth to dawn.

        A SONG   Sue McCown

        She sang -
        The notes of her song
        Trembled over the stillness of the quiet room.
        The moving trees stopped their swaying motions
        To listen; the gray skies lifted their somber shades
        And gave way to the sweetness of her tones.
        What notes are these which bring such reign?
        Is it of castles, of kings, of knights?
        Of ventures unknown to the common realm?
        No! The notes sing of love -
        Of unsatisfied love. A romance
        That gave and never received.
        A love that re-echoes in one's lonely heart.
        A love that is guided by one's inner thoughts,
        By one's heart and soul.
        And as the notes hung o'er the pensive air,
        The trees and the skies knew the sad little song
        And tried with their souls
        To return the unanswered love.

        THE ROSE OF MY HEART   Maureen Loop

        There grows afar a sweet, pink rose
        With petals dew empearled.
        Its fragrance fills my lonely heart
        With love for all the world.

        And now this rose, though wilted long,
        With fragrance strangely soft
        Still fills my lonely room,
        Lifting my soul aloft.

CHALLENGE   Shirley Anne Roeger

Knowledge:
A guiding light
Casting its beam among
Youth bringing a brighter future
For all.

BENEDICTION   Jean-Marie Boyd

The tree stretched forth its green-tipped arms,
To greet the new-born day
And softly sighed a breezy psalm
To praise Divinity.

God heard the humble whispered hymn,
And so well pleased was He,
He told the sun to kiss each leaf
And thank His loving tree.

Caressingly the sun beamed down;
I saw it kiss that tree
And as God's blessing fell on it,
It fell also on me.

WAR   Bill Matheson

The blast of a gun,
The death of a man;
One less enemy,
One more widow
Or childless mother:
This is war.
The wounded and dying
Lie in trenches and foxholes,
The dead and dismembered
Lie in bloody heaps.
I kill you
Unless you kill me first.
Bursting bombs,
Exploding shells,
Blasts from mines;
Fire, shrapnel, and blood all about:
This is war.
Scientists in laboratories, workers in factories,
All working towards ultimate destruction;
But why, do they know?

248

IN MEMORIAM   Mike McLain

A rickety garage.
A board loose here; one pane of glass in window cracked,
One gone; the ancient sagging door on one weak hinge;
Paint or whitewash, long past, chipped off and forgotten.

Last spring they leaned a trellis on the rickety garage
And resurrected seeds from some musty, dusty
                        attic hiding place
To plant them in soft earth around its base:
The roses grew to cling in rapt disguise
Upon a termite-eaten, rickety garage.
Those roses will mark it where it dies . . .
An aged wooden building's last corsage.

SONNET I   Elizabeth Loving

A day in autumn doth my heart enthrall,
Like to the swelling of a little stream;
Yet colors are the brightest of it all
As if my heart has given me a dream.

Some poets sing of glories of the spring
When for themselves the joys of life unfold;
But I prefer to feel - as if a king,
And on a slope a symphony behold;

A symphony of color that I see;
The leaves of gold the rustling wind doth fling,
And little birdies hopping in the trees,
And all at once I feel as if to sing.

Thus color comes and thus it goes away;
Oh, for the thrills of a glorious autumn day!

HOMESICKNESS   Laurence Richardson Taylor

A magic land I've never seen,
With purpled lakes and forests green,
Lies o'er the sea, and far away,
Many a mile and sailing day,
A gentle place, so fresh and clean,
A land I've never seen.

A land of mountains rising high,
Where meets the tower with the sky,
Where yet it seems that I have been,
Within the forests, dark and green,
Alas, 'tis true, homesick am I,
For a land I've never seen.

AUTUMN   Elizabeth Rowland

Yellow leaves
Prepare to transfer their color
                to the solemn earth.
Black fingers
Wind themselves through the brilliant expanse
                struggling to dominate.

Time wears on;
Cold and wind become more intense;
One by one
The yellow leaves turn dark with effort
                and regretfully take flight to the earth
Leaving hope with the coming of spring.

MYSTERIOUS CHANCE   Shirley Cosby

Beyond the realm of human cognizance
Where mundane minds would hesitate to tread,
There dwells the overawing Prince of Chance,
Who weaves into the loom of life a thread.

Despair and bliss comprise this thread so sure,
And lives are spun by you in fickle haste.
Because our sight of you is so obscure,
You care not whether you shall meet our taste.

You are possessor of the sharpest sword,
O sever suffering, and weave but bliss!
Confer on us the best you can afford;
Bestow on us felicity with a kiss.

Now Prince! I must conclude, and I entreat
You snip despair and all men, smiling, greet.

THE PURPLE IRIS   Laura Jean Heins

There are irises blooming
By the garden gate
Amidst the green foliage
Standing tall and straight.
They wear the majestic color
Of a king's garment,
And from the velvet petals
Comes a delicate scent.

Oh purple is the amethyst
And clinging is the rose,
But the iris reigns in my heart
Independently it grows.

THE TRUSTING TREE   Jack Davidson

God has a special purpose for me;
I am a tree;
He told me to lose my leaves in the fall,
And during the winter have no protection at all;
He also told me to have hope in my heart,
And when spring comes round,
He would give me a new start.

YOUNG GUY CROONER   Diane St. Jean

All I want is the robin's song
And the rain in my hair, and I'm happy;
My arm around a pretty girl,
And a suit that's sharp and snappy.
Let me smell a dark pink rose,
A good old American Beauty;
To love my love and kiss a hand
'S my one and only duty.
Oh, all I want's the bluebird's song
And a rainbow or a moon beam
And love and life and happiness
And that's my every dream.

THE AGED   Russell Homer Bruegger

Wrinkled, scarred, and grey!
Sitting, just sitting all day!
Can't do much, waiting, just waiting
For God to take them away!

Looking with a gleam!
Who knows what those eyes have seen?
The things that that body withstood
Are but now some distant dream.

They too were once young!
They romped and played and had fun,
Grew up, and with all their hearts loved.
But now they're old, and all is done!

All they knew has gone!
The future lies somewhere beyond!
They know they have not long to go,
But still they want to hold on.

They are the aged!

SPRING   Mary Murray

Hues reach across the sky and
To the earth bend near,
Pines stand tall and straight
Lifting a perfume clear.

Clouds are soft and fleecy white
Drifting in the blue,
Brooks are babbling unknown words
In their joy anew.

LAMENTED GOWN   Dede Shetter

Early spring trees,
Their cob-web limbs
Entwined in fragile lace of green,
As spring frolics past
Delicately fringed branches are no longer,
But in their place a fine green fabric
Rich in weave; bold in pattern.
But alas - in exclusion
The weeping willow still in her lacy gown.
She wanted a lush garment too.
That is why she weeps
And bows her pretty head.
Foolish maid - does she not know
Her gown is most exquisite of them all?

GOD'S BUSY ANGELS   Carolyn Skeen

The sun goes down behind the trees,
And softly blows the evening breeze;
Then God's little angels, tiptoeing light,
Go pulling down the shades of night.
They paint the moon with gold and yellow,
Then fluff the clouds for heaven's pillow;
Then getting ready for a night of play,
They feast upon the milkyway.

As they return from a trip to Mars,
Each one drinks from the dipper of stars.
And as the rain comes falling down
They ride a rain drop to the ground;
But when the sun is shining through
The angels bid this earth adieu,
And eyes all full of worldly gleam,
Climb back to heaven on a gold sunbeam.

THE BRUSH AND MY HAIR   Juanita Jean Ruck

Down my dark hair
Through my soft curls
Tended with care
Are their glamourous swirls.

Up in an up-sweep
Down in a bob
Easy to keep
And a wonderful job.

THE DOORS OF LIFE   Joseph Brennan

Down the long corridors of life,
In love or hate, in peace or strife,
Through many doorways I must go,
And each door leads to bliss or woe.

Some doors that open up for me
Bring hours of fun and jollity;
And days of gray and solemn hue,
Lie beyond some portals too.

When doors swing wide for vice and sin,
O keep me, God, from ent'ring in;
And let me find security,
Through doors of home that welcome me.

When at the end of life's brief span,
I face the portal that each man
Must pass, may Thy angels come to me,
And lead me through that door to Thee.

AN ASSIGNMENT   Bob Demaroy

I don't know how to start this thing,
    I don't know what to say.
But tomorrow a poem I should bring,
    And so I must write it today.

I could start out like all the rest,
    With a bird, a flower, or a tree.
But Burns and Dickens did their best,
    So there's not much chance for me.

This is the end; I'm nearly through;
    My thoughts have all departed.
But if I had written as the others do,
    This poem had ne'er been started.

ODE TO THE HEAVENS   Penny Freedman

Fathomless omnicolored deep,
Mysterious neighbor to the sea,
Home of clouds and rain,
Abiding place for moon and sun and stars,
Originator of night; cold, black, starspeckled,
Founder of seasons, indeed creator of life,
Is there no end to your boundlessness?

Upon your countenance plays a drama of emotions,
From storm clouds, a roar of anger,
Gentle zephyrs, whispering of love,
Streaks of lightning revealing hidden pangs of hatred,
Joy and happiness radiating from the twinkling gems
                                                                of night.

O, Guardian of starry hosts,
Of souls from all mankind,
Dictator of time and space,
Am I always to be puzzled by your presence?

A MOMENT'S REGRESSION   Ronald Chamberlain

Awaken in the dead of night
You know not why.
Awaken in the cold sweat of fright
And wonder as you lie
What neanderthal instinct awakened you;
And why you lie afraid to move
Afraid of the dark, and of the things
That move, and creep, and kill
                    in the dark . . .
And then, the kitten, that so softly
                    entered, purrs.

HOME   Caroline Tighe

A city beyond the call of the wild
Yet close enough to be inspired
Seems to me to represent
A city of desire.

Where homes are few
And far between
Where only hotels show,
There you'll find
A heart of stone.
But where you find
A house, a home,
There you'll find
A heart of gold.

THE RIVER WAITING FOR THE MOON   Lyle Martin

The river is quiet,
Waiting for the big silver moon
To dance and play upon the water -
To laugh and sing upon the water -
The moon playing shadows on the water.
The river sings - happy and gay.

YOUTH LOST   William Maloney

If youth's form could but endure
    While life adds year to year,
Then worried brow and aged smile
    Would change to youthful cheer.
And crippled legs and stiffened
    Hands would nimbly ply,
And aged hearts and feeble
    At youth no more would sigh.
What a world of happy hearts
    What a time of childlike joy.
If our parents and their parents
    Would once more be girl or boy.

A CITY   Loree Stager

A city
Built by calloused hands and sweating backs.
A city,
Making up for all it lacks.

A city, like any city,
Neither large nor small.
A city with its share of good and bad
With its buildings both short and tall.

A city in a country
Broad and wide.
Built by people
With hearts of pride.

A city cradling families
Of today and tomorrow.
A city showing always
Its joys and sorrow.

A city,
Built of block and stone.
A city known only by those
Who call it home.

SEA MOODS   Kay Hall

Neptune is angry, he rants and he raves,
Crescendo increases with each pounding wave
The gale cackles wildly as ships overturn,
And deeper, and angrier, the stormy sea churns.
The screams of poor sailors, add horrible fright
And the gleam from the lighthouse is lost in the night.
The wind is abating, its wildness is vent,
The morning will dawn on a sea fully spent
Boards will lie on the sandy beach,
Broken and rotting and starting to bleach.
The moods of Old Neptune change with day.
Either angry or sleeping or at impish play
Now the face of the sea is a clear, sparkly green,
Now ominous with blackness and dull gray sheen
To watch is to see a cycle of life
The peace, the happiness, hatred and strife.

DEATH   Roberta Charlotte Katz

A fog-covered, cobbled street,
A fly-specked windowpane crouched above,
A faucet dripping its monstrous melody,
While the restaurants are no longer places
          where people meet.
The darkened hollow now empty of those who love,
The whole world now just dark and sooty,
The city ominous in its lack of noise,
The el and subway are now long stilled;
The world is now at peace and rest
Wrapped in the arms of eternal death.

WHO?   Nancy McCall

Who are the soldiers of the night,
      Enshrouded in the dark?
Who makes the shadows in the vale,
      And holds the meadow lark?
Who looks into the blue each day -
      And hails the gentle breeze?
God made them, loves them,
      Lives above them,
Mortals call them Trees.

MUSIC Mary Alice Hall

I wonder what my life would be
If I had never heard a song?
If brooks murmured no melody,
If trees swayed not in harmony,
If crashing waves rolled not at sea,
If no bird sang the whole day long,
I wonder what my life would be
If I had never heard a song?

SEPTEMBER Robin Van Loben Sels

Harvest moon, with golden splendor,
Brings the month of crisp September.
Tangy mornings, spiced with frost,
Fields with summer yields are crossed.
Pumpkins ripen, trees grow old,
Nights grow longer, clearer, cold.
Harvest moon, with golden splendor,
Brings the month of crisp September.

WHO IS MY BROTHER? Judith Krahmer

Who is my brother?
Is he my mother's son?
My uncle or my cousin?
Is he my brother? Only he?
No.

Well, who is my brother?
Those who have blond hair,
And blue eyes, like me?
Are they my brothers? Only they?
No.

Then who is my brother?
The people who go to my church
Or speak my language?
Are these my brothers? Only these?
No.

Who then are my brothers?
The white man, the black and yellow?
Mohammedan, Christian and Jew?
Are these my brothers? Are these?
Yes.

DREAMS   Susan Myler

To look at clouds as they pass by,
To gaze into the deep blue sky,
To hope so hard perhaps in vain,
For dreams are lost like drops of rain;
To build a hope in empty air,
That proves so bleak but looked so fair,
To look at the world with eyes so clear,
Eyes that are opened and free from fear -
All this is good, but one must learn
That reality is our first concern!

THE WORTHWHILE THINGS   Frances Ella Reedy

Some things in life cannot be bought or sold,
The beauty of these cannot be told.
The fragrance of pines on a sunny day,
Beautiful flowers that bloom in May.
Chimes ringing out on the evening breeze,
The purple of mountains and the blue of the seas.
White clouds that float in a deep blue sky,
Priceless things that money cannot buy.

Sunlight shining on a field of grain,
Windy days and the patter of rain.
White ruffled curtains stirring in the breeze,
Mockingbirds singing and the hum of the bees.
Organ music swelling, now soft, now loud;
Willow trees standing with their heads bowed.
Horses grazing in a pasture green,
And the beauty of other things unseen.

AT WORK   Robert Bolgard

Man
At work
Polishing his convertible.

Fog
At work
Undoing man's industry.

God
At work
Growing mighty forests.

Man
At work
Undoing God's industry.

A JOURNEY   Evelyn Curfman

Where am I going? I really don't know,
Down to the meadow where the buttercups grow,
Or up on the knoll where the strong winds blow,
Anywhere, anywhere, I hardly know.

Where shall I go as the clouds roll by?
White ones, blue ones up in the sky.
What shall I do as the dark shadows pass?
Giant ones, dwarf ones over the grass.

Where am I going? I hardly know,
What matters it anyway where mortals go.
Out to the forest where the bluebells grow,
Anywhere, anywhere, why should you know.

THE GRASS   Allen Tarro

The grass has so little to do -
A blade of simple green.
It holds the sunshine in its lap,
And bows to everything.
It stirs all day to pretty tunes
When breezes blow along.
It dwells in lonely places
And dreams the days away.

The grass has so little to do.
I'm glad I am not
A blade of simple green.

NATURE'S SONG   Patricia Comstock

As tree tops linger in the sky
          and winds blow through so free;
The steeples reach to kiss the night,
          the sands rush down to the sea;
The bells ring out the glory gone,
          and future years to come;
The moon, the stars are all so gay,
          but brightest of all is the sun;
As clouds roll by they wake the stars,
          they twinkle at the light,
For they can see the whole wide world,
          on such a beautiful night.

AVIS   Marvin Rountree Cox

Avoid, sunsets, bel ami;
They are symbolic of too many things.
They hold the qualities of every twilight -
Too marked by sentiment to bear
Much weight on the advancing night.

Proud beauty is suggested,
And to see
Is not to grasp completely,
Bel ami.

SORROW AND JOY   Arlene Malcom

The sorrow of our lives
Is balanced by the joy that we know.
When we really stop and think
Our sorrow isn't half what we make it.
We all should know that "into each life some rain must
                                        fall."
Then someone says, "Yes, but too much has fallen in
                                        mine."
That person has forgotten all the joy
That he, or she, has ever experienced.
He has forgotten the joy of a bright spring day,
With its rich green grass, budding and blooming flowers,
          the leafing trees,
And the pure joy of living on such a day;
Forgotten the joy of a child picking bright colored flowers;
The joy of a mother when her baby takes
Its first step, or says its first word;
The joy of a girl in her first formal going to her first
          real dance;
And the joy of a bride and groom
Facing life together through sorrow and joy.
The sorrow of today is more than balanced by the joy of
                                        tomorrow.

THE STREAM   Ned Coon

Through the rapids, down the mountains,
From the snows, out of the fountains.
Scurrying, hurrying by the peaks,
Swirling, hurling, down it streaks.
Down the falls, to the distant hills.
On to the gently rolling rills.
Faster, vaster on it sallies
Lower, lower, through the valleys,
Ever growing, ever slowing, ever moving,
          ever flowing.

ONLY TODAY   Sherry Ennis

Yesterday's sun went down last night,
With only memories left of its flight;
Yesterday's sorrow and happiness it seems
Is only a memory left for our dreams.
Who knows in the morning what the new day will bring;
Will it be worth living, or just a passing thing?
Why should we long for a day that is past;
When new hopes and adventures lie in our grasp?
Today our blessings may seem trifling and small,
But tomorrow they'll be precious and greatest of all.
Today we should reach a goal we have set,
So tomorrow we'll rejoice instead of regret.

WHEAT   Wilma Oaks

A field of wheat --
Grass in abundance.
Majestic, flourishing,
Rippled by a breeze rhythmically rolling across it.
Glorious, lustrous,
Shimmering in the golden daybreak.
Solemn, dramatic, dignified,
Rustling, in the soft, sheer shafts of moonlight.
Courageous, sturdy,
Progressing even beneath snow and ice ...
Ever ready to produce food for humanity.
Firm, secure,
Rooted deep in the earth;
Exemplifying endurance and perseverance.
Thousands of slender, graceful heads,
Copper-crowned,
Look into the heavens
In search of their Maker.

AUTUMN   Regina Buono

When burnished leaves come tumbling down,
Off trees with merry dancing.
When pumpkins flourish from the ground,
Their orangey charm entrancing.
When Hallowe'eners beg for treats,
In costumes bright and gay,
They get their candies and sweet meats
Without a long delay.
For it is autumn time once more,
The world, a frosty place.
When there are happy times galore,
And holidays set pace.

WHAT IS SEEN   Frank Jolly

I see the city lights,
Shining and twinkling like pinpoints of starlight
In the velvet night.
I see trains crawling;
Turning, twisting like quaint, smoking, roaring reptiles.
I see trucks moving like burdened ants, carrying
                    terrific loads.
I see all of these.
And do I see ugliness?
Or do I look beyond to see
The beauty in all this industry.

THIS WORLD   Janet Dunlap

Oh Why - why is our world like this -
Oh why must we fight a greater force -
A greater force than us.

Why do so many of us miss -
The wonder and beauty
Of a quiet and peaceful life.
The beauty of Love and Laughter
In a peaceful life.

Why for our rights -
Must we battle each and other -
And not see our children grow
In a world of beauty
But in a world of War and Hatred.

Our life will not be rich and full
Till we have seen the beauty of Peace.

                              Herbert U. Jones, Jr.

Where, when the time comes,
    Shall I make my bed?
In a bird's nest far up the sky
Or between the rocks of my
    garden wall?
Shall I melt into the rich warm red
    on a painter's palette
Or the cold blue of an iceberg
    in Arctic seas
And then melt on into Arctic seas?
Will it be in a place of golden
    streets
Or of roaring fires and pitchforks,
Or in a bird's nest far up the sky?

THE SEA   Anita Ann Forbeck

The sea at once a thing of beauty and terror,
A highway dividing and a very great barrier.

In exultation of its sunlit moods and fathomless deeps,
Here alone great marvelous mysteries sleep.

If it weren't for this wonder we would not be,
For 'life itself emerged from the sea.

No other world has this great blessing,
Some are too cold to have us guessing.

Mars has ice caps, some moisture, but no sea,
And on Mercury no water seems to be.

The sea is a world all in itself,
From the deep canyons to the continantal shelf.

PLAYMATE   Sharon Olson

I saw a kite today,
A little boy holding it tight.
He let out the string this way - that way,
And soon it was out of sight.

I saw a kite today,
Up in the sky so blue.
It wagged its tail this way - that way,
I know it was playing with you.

I saw a kite today,
Bright yellow and golden brown.
It took a bow this way - that way,
I know it wanted to come down.

THE WIND IS PLAYING PEEK-A-BOO Carol Blau

The Wind is playing peek-a-boo.
Its childish whistlings blowing round -
It's huffing - puffing down the town,
It's playing hopscotch on a cloud,
It climbs a roof and laughs aloud.
It slides and scurries -
Skips and hurries -
It rattles at a window casement ...
Whispers in a lonely basement.
Juggles papers on its nose
And ties the sky in bright blue bows -
The wind is playing peek-a-boo ....

MY LOVE FOR THEE — Elvira Beattie

As constant as an ocean's loud crashing,
As spacious as the heavens above,
As true as the daily sun rising,
As natural as the beauteous moon,
As pure as sweet dew in the morning,
As wistful as a moaning wind,
As natural as the beauteous moon,
As pure as sweet dew in the morning,
As wistful as a moaning wind,
As undemanding as a pale blue sky,
As steadfast as the moss-ridden earth,
As holy as an uplifted prayer -
My love for thee.

NIGHT LIGHTS — Sandra Lee Ball

On calm, clear nights I see the lights
Shining across the bay.
They twinkle awhile, seeming to smile,
And flee at the break of day.
Each white light seems as fair as moonbeams
That fall from the heavenly sky;
And even the wind that comes drifting in
Can't make them fade and pass by.

They laugh at the ships and if they had lips
Would bid them a soft farewell,
As they slowly pass on the river of glass,
In reply to the tune of their bell.
Soon they take flight with the passing of night
And the breaking of each new dawn.
For the early breath of the morning brings death
And they in a twinkle are gone.

TO A CHILD — Suzanne Zuercher

The joy of it!
The sudden vital interest
All-consuming in its moment.
The ever-changing, ever-shifting
portrait
Of a living, breathing world.

Then sorrow,
Fleeting as a new mood, comes
To thrust this joy from a simple,
unmixed mind.

All things are new to you,
And all things, wonderful!

CURIOUS THINGS   Carol Jay Cope

Curious things make up a person's memories
Curious things, yes, curious things
A shaggy white dog and crinkly leaves
That walk up the stairs of a new fall breeze
Curious things, yes curious things.

Curious things make up a person's childhood
Curious things, yes curious things
A three year old birthday and a bright red hood
That came at Christmas for being good.
Curious things, yes curious things.

Curious things make up a person's mind.
Curious things, yes, curious things.
A brittle answer, a retort unkind.
That's so harsh you leave all tears behind.
Curious things, yes, curious things.

Curious, yes curious is all life.
The tears, the heartache, the bitter strife
The joy cutting thru like a well honed knife
Curious, yes, curious is all life.

OPPORTUNITY   Sonya M. Reichvalder

"What am I bid for this valuable?"
Asks the hurried auctioneer called Time.
From the rear an enormous sum is heard.
"Do I hear any more?" again shouts Time.
"Going, going, gone!" The one high bidder
Grabbed his valuable, opportunity,
Because he knew Time would wait no longer.

Frances Zapatka

Life:
A candy-coated
Bitter herb,
So rich, so sweet
And yet,
So stranglingly bitter.

Methinks:
I'll not bite another
Morsel.

DESERTED   Larry Jones

A house that is built for the rich and proud,
And parties gay and free,
Is a beautiful sight on a moonlight night,
A beautiful sight to see.

But when it is left to crumble and fall,
And there's no one to care,
You wonder why such a beautiful prize
Was left with no one there.

What sorrow and shame, what grief and woe
Did fall on this house so bare?
For those who knock on its rattling door
Will find that there's no one there.

REBIRTH   Barbara Nyberg

When playful winds of spring awake old earth
With magic song, and winter's ghostly gloom
Is swept away, the skies behold with mirth
The drowsy meadows stirred by sudden bloom.

Ere long the gorgeous queen of summer reigns,
And dying autumn withers in its wake
The fruits of former days, while nature feigns
Delight and masks with art her one mistake.

Then snowflakes dance across drab field and town,
And winter hides beneath her regal cloak
The barren earth, which, groomed in silver gown,
Awaits the birth of spring and flower folk.

Like seasons men enact the play of life
And death - to be reborn with childish spring.

THE PATHWAY TO CONTENTMENT
                            Kay Season
A life of joy, success, and ease
Is always promised those who please
To keep alert and try to catch
The opportunities that hatch
Within the fertile minds of those
Upon whose thumb the callous shows.
And those whose vigor and all-seeing glance
Will never let them miss the chance
To try with all their heart and soul
To reach their highly-honored goal.

The pathway to the life of ease
Is paved by everyone of these -
And many more.

THE GIFT   Arline Anderson

Shining sunlight sifts slowly through the branches
Which burst with bright blossoms,
Crisp, tingling air stimulates the spirits.
Such a day in spring is sought after by many –
But the lifeless, spiritless body below
Oblivious to the grandeur of the day
Never more will witness spring,
For he has been laid on the altar of Mars
Giving his life for those who now watch
Shining sunlight siftly slowly through the branches.

TOMORROW   Joanne Gage

Tomorrow is a word: a philosophy;
A twisted line on a page; a philosophy;
Making a weary world look up
          for tomorrow.

Tomorrow is America: a dream;
A home for all the homeless; a dream;
Keeping a country great, waiting
          for tomorrow.

Tomorrow is a temple: a refuge;
A place that is a promise; a refuge;
A n excuse for us, who cannot face
          today.

SHORES   Dorothy Jackson

Will it be the same to all of them,
Returning to their shore,
To hear the sound of distant surf,
Crashing with a roar?
And will they all come home again,
With mem'ry fresh and clean,
Of hills and farms and families,
Of future things to dream?

Or will they still remember of
The nights so full of death,
And days that could not ever bring
A clean and living breath?
The guns, the roar, the stench of those
Not living anymore,
But they will meet, yes, once again,
As friends – on a distant shore.

WHITE LIMBS   James Duemmel

The planetree towers o'er the whispering brook,
　　　Rooted there in drenched earth to grow,
Shedding autumn's bronzed and stiffened leaves
　　　(Wrinkled vessels for the creek below),
Uplifting, against the star-strewn midnight-blue,
　　　Ivory boughs, unkempt, and slim, that glow
With the silver splashed on every rippling swell,
　　　That sigh and moan when the breezes of winter blow.

A STATE OF HEART   Bonnie Amrich

Confusion is a state of mind;
Love, a state of heart.
Yet confusion is to blame
For keeping Two apart.

Two who know they are in love
And share this state of heart,
But cannot overcome the cause
That keeps them both apart.

How is it that the mind, not heart,
Can keep these Two apart?
Perhaps some day one will win out,
I hope it is the heart!

OUR HOME   Mary Kay Panisko

Come in the evening, or
Come in the morning,
Come when you're looked for,
Come without warning.
For our house is warm, happy and gay
Just come to our house,
Any time of the day.

At night the children
Sit around by the fire,
While father tells stories,
Hour after hour.

Yes, you will look far,
To find a house like ours,
Warm, happy and gay.
Just come to our house,
Our happy house,
Any time of the day.

AS GOES THE WIND   Delajane Yates

Passing as goes the wind
Softly unnoticed,
Spring and summer pass;
And then, autumn comes
So soon to forsake;
For winter
In her silent way betakes upon herself a timid way
To erase the warm and golden hue
And crown herself supreme and cool,
And with slow and perfect timing,
She passes
As goes the wind.

ALPHA AND OMEGA   Sally Cutter

I am Alpha and Omega; the beginning and the end,
I am the Creator,
                    the Ruler,   the Judge,
My whisper is heard in the sigh of the trees;
My wrath resounds in the rumble of thunder;
My laughter dwells in the sound of little brooks;
My caress is felt in the soothing breeze;

I am the Architect who designed the world;
I am the Artist who painted the sky;
I am the Builder who hollowed the vales;
I am the Sculptor who chiseled the hills;
I am the Farmer who planted the earth;
I am the Electrician who lighted the sun;
I am God who created man.
I am Alpha and Omega; the beginning and the end,
I am the Creator,
                    the Ruler,
                              the Judge.

RESISTANCE   William Anderson

Classic story
Whose plot is old,
Simple and yet divine.
Crude it seems
And humble too,
That ancient tale
Of wholesomeness,
That fights so hard
Those clutching hands
Of degeneration.

FALL IN MULESHOE   Helen Stovall

Fall is here,
Everyone smells and sees it.
The smoke of the burr-pit is foul and monotonous,
But the more the better! because,
It brings news of a bountiful harvest.

Fall is here,
Leaves cover the ground.
Not like others, so colorful and beautiful,
But still they crackle merrily,
At the cotton-trailers touch.

WITH EACH NEW DAY   Joan Maransky

What makes the soul awake
And rise to meet the day?
From whence does one obtain
Desire to face what e'er the hour may bring -
Fascinated by thoughts of things to come?

'Tis that surprise that holds attention;
'Tis that surprise that each new day brings;
For, on each morn, each man may know
That day will bring a happening unforeseen
To add that spice or grieve the heart
To make complete the life he leads.

TRANSITION   Carlisle Beery

New wines
From vines
And harp tunes beckon me;

An olive
And olive branch
Swaying in motion.

On wing
A dove says,
"Come, oh come,
You may taste, then eat,
And flee."

"Wines from vines are sweet ....
You taste!
Catch an olive from some twig.
Then escape to better sights.
To better sights
Than even these!"

THE MIGHTIEST SWORD　　Vesta Sue Rhodes

Last night I read a book;
The author dipped his pen into a lake of fire
And seared raw facts of life
Into my soul and dragged it through earth's mire.
Somehow I knew his mind was warped,
To him all love was lust and God a jest;
That night in my disturb'ed slumber
My fevered brain sought, but found no rest.

And now I read another book;
This author dips his pen in truth - the mightiest sword,
And through his kindness, devotion, love
Leads me to know his friend - the Lord.

TRAGEDY　　Priscilla Dawkins

Now the swallow spiralled down,
Shuddered once, then lay still;
The tightening of my saddened heart,
Final frenzy of tiny bill,
Spoke each their grim futility.
A sudden laugh, a patter of feet
Made me turn. Near defeat
Of all my faith in man and life
Came when I saw the urchin's face;
No least remorse nor inner strife
Could I see - only what must be
Exultation. Only God
And he and I and the sardonic sod
In all the world were there to see
The monstrous deed. He turned to flee;
Swift words welled up - now, bid him stay!
They froze, unuttered. He ran away.
Who was I to alter fate
When nearly every nation, state,
Cowered each behind its battlements -
Each man, almost, behind his bristling gun -
Who was I to silence even one.

HILLS　　　　　　　　Evelyn Eberhardt

The Hills
Stand tall and proud
Like Kings upon their thrones
A golden presence in the midst
Of light.

EARLY DEATH   Emmett S. Thompson

It rains
And the cold pools of water are mirrors of the soul
For it is winter and the songbirds are gone.

But the song remains to taunt of the summer.

You, too, are gone --- and the song is only words
                    without meaning
Sung to a corpse.

For I am gone . . . Without the song, the summer,
                    or the birds, or you
I am the corpse.

And the song becomes a funeral dirge.

WHY WORK!   Ruth Gilmore

'Tis surely a beautiful morning,
The sun has just kissed the dew.
The road has the pink of the dawning,
And the sky is a glorious blue.

The thought of a trip to the country,
Or a hike by a trickling stream,
Today is not just a reality,
Or a poor housewife's dream.

Toss aside your mop and your scrubbrush,
Open up the door -
Mother Nature is waiting,
Who could ask for more!

WHY   Vera Wells

You ask me why I love you?
It's simpler far to say
Why the grass accepts the dew
Or noon consumes the day.

You wonder how I love you?
More easily explain
Why the hyacinth is blue,
Why silver slants the rain.

You question when I love you?
Can there be a measured chime
By which love keeps a curfew?
Love is for the end of time.

THE WORLD   Carroll Hall

This endless bell with echoes to eternity,
The tones of time which move all souls to motion,
Is the force of world and universe and Diety
And thought - and bells of gold emotion.
I hear the waters of the clearest melody,
Flowing over time-worn wisdom rocks,
The world is reality,
And seeing through the self; then beauty knocks.
The bell of nature rings a beauty song,
And tones of contemplation thin the air,
With higher gathered echoes of the flowing gong:
In a bell of nature - eternity is there.
Water is clearly moving over rocks of aged soul,
And the world - a mellow masterpiece of supersoul,
Is like the bell which sends a golden roll
Of music o'er the green laid happy knoll.
The man a supersoul - the greatest beauty of The Lord,
The world a bell of harmony and great design of time,
What mortal soul can afford
Not to listen - and by goodness not to Heaven climb.

CONCERT   Marie-Anne Howard

The orchestra tunes up
          a harmony of discord.
The conductor steps to the podium,
Raises his gleaming baton.
Then,
Flight from the work-a-day world,
          of trials and tribulations
Flight, to a magic world,
Where there is only the mood of the music,
I rest!

THE COMING OF WINTER   Therese Fecher

North winds blow ever harder
     The leaves have flown away,
The hours of day have shortened
     And the nights are cold and grey.

From out of Fall has sprung
     Winter - in icy bliss
Scattering through the land - Frost,
     Unwary plants to kiss.

SATAN IS REAL   Frances White

By the evil forces that we know each day,
By the hurting things that we say,
By the stinging, leering glances,
By our haughty, pride-filled prances,
By our failure to tell others,
By how we need not bother,
By the deceitful lies we tell,
By the woven wicked spell,
By these and all the ills we feel,
By this we know that Satan is real.

PRELUDES   Francia Gott

Everything in life has its prelude.
Each piece by Chopin, beethoven and Bach.
The start of every opera.
The tryout of a new dessert
          before Mother's bridge club.
The Constitution has its preamble.
Each speech - an introduction.
Each means of locomotion - a test run.
The atomic weapons have their proving ground.
The movies have previews.
All life but life itself
          has its prelude.

TRIBUTE TO A PASSING SPECIES
                              R. T. Thornberry

Impatiently it hoots again,
A lantern cuts an arc,
The monster grips the shining steel,
Its eye darts through the dark,
The slipping grasp at last secure,
Its bellows scream, "Beware!"
Its hoary breaths stab through the black,
A beast departs its lair.

And now it trudges, now it trots,
The earth quails and quakes,
And now it gallops, now it streaks
Past forests, fields and lakes.
Defiant cries from deep, black lungs
Are threats to maim and kill;
Mad mastodon with fiery gleam,
What dare oppose thy will?

DEATH   Diane Mendes

To some the thought of Death is a haunting, black,
And terrible spectre, nightly coming to fill
Their dreams with phantoms that will never be still,
Though banished by day with work, it then comes back
At night, with dismal horrors which never lack
The power to keep one lying fright'ned, till
At last there comes a dream of cries so shrill,
And nameless forms dark draped in somber sack.
An honest man has no such fear as this:
He knows that Death with him walks as a friend,
Though it may take away those that he will miss,
And forever close the door which Life had opened,
It leads to distant lands of eternal bliss.
He knows that Death is a beginning, not an end.

SONNET   Geri Oppenheim

Dear God, I'd like to hear today, that war
Has ceased; the cannons stilled; and hope renewed;
So all may share the Season's joys, imbued
With "Peace on Earth, Good Will," for ever more.

This pray'r is heard on near and distant shore
In many lands, in churches grand or crude.
Our verdict now: it's time this world-wide feud
Must end; and "Peace on Earth, Good Will" restore.

The world is rousing from this futile trance
That strife has always left as aftermath.
Let's pray this Christmas start our Renaissance,
Dispelling hate and war's unholy wrath,
Resuming Faith and Trust; and life enhance
With "Peace on Earth, Good Will" to light our path.

THE SEARCH   James Fulton

In the sphere of truth
My search holds sway;
It's ne'er behind me
Night nor day;
I sail uncharted
To unknown shores -

I move through the ages
And pass the stare
Of ancient sages;
Yet when mists unfold
In the gleam of ageless knowledge
My own image I behold!

TIME   Joan M. Demyan

What is an hour, what is a day?
    Just some time that is drifting away.
What is a week, a month, or a year?
    Only a life with a laugh and a tear.

Ten years - a decade - and centuries roll,
    No body, no heart, but always a soul;
Each fleeting moment I know is mine,
    But eternity can not be measured in time.

YOUTH! GIVE EAR!   Margaret Berry

I have cursed and I have hated
This strange entanglement
Of evil thoughts and sinful nights,
Of hours wrongly spent.

Oh youth, who have used these methods
To give your vigor vent,
Fall on your knees and pray to God
For power to repent!

SWIRLING SKIRTS   Mary Maney

Stately and tall
    The ballerina stands,
Gracefully poised,
    Are her beautiful hands.

Now on the stage
    Smoothly she floats,
On her toes, in bourree'
    To softly played notes.

Pas de basque to the left,
    Pas de basque to the right,
Now she turns, now she whirls,
    Now she glides into light.

With a smile on her face,
    Rhythm in her toes,
Glissade, arabesque, pirouette
    And then pose.

FOR ALL THESE   Barbara Young

For those who love the setting and rising sun,
For those who love a blazing fire,
For those who love the beautiful music,
For those who love the moving sea,
For those who can live in the dark and in the quiet,
I give thee peace.
For those who love a forest and its creatures,
For those who think in beauty,
For those who dream of happiness,
For those who live with love,
For all these, I give peace.
Let not the creeds of
The moderns take peace's place.

THE CARPENTER   Judith Burrows

One morning
I passed the shop of the Gentle Carpenter.
It was a sunny place ...
And there He spent His days
Making boats and benches and toys.

I stopped there
And He invited me to step inside
To watch Him shape a piece of wood.
He said if I wanted to play, I could ...
And ask questions ... and sing.

I wondered
What it was that made Him smile ...
Then I knew.
He shaped not only boughs of pine,
But children's hearts in tender ways.

LIFE AND DEATH   Philip Thieme

Life and death walk hand in hand
Death beside each man doth stand
Time will pass and death must come
But death is rest and peace to some.
Life is no more than a dream.
Death is really life's great goal
No one lives except to die.
So pass the days and do your best

Add whatever you can so that
The world may be a better place.
The wind may whisper, flowers may
              bloom,
And life and death may still walk --
Hand in hand together.

TO BEAUTY   Mary Elsie Robertson

Ah Beauty, thou enchantress of men's souls,
Thou will-o'-the-wisp that drags men on a never-ending search,
Why is it that we can never quite capture you?
In the golden moment before dawn we glimpse you,
But the moment is gone and you are lost!
Perhaps it is because you know, oh wise one,
That if we could drink our fill at your nectar springs,
Man would but become drunk,
And die.

WHAT'S IN A SONG   Billy Warrick

What's in a song?
A melody,
That causes man's heart to beat faster,
And makes joy and happiness his master?

What's in a song?
Some strange bewitching force
That holds within its realm
The power to make for man an earthly
                                    heaven

HOW EASY TO WRITE A POEM!
                          Bertha Huerta

My fingernails are bitten off,
My mouth is full of foam,
For I was told two weeks ago
That I must write a poem.

My nerves are all a frazzle
And my brain's completely blank
The little things I do think up
Just fall back with a clank.

I'll fly a kite, jump in a lake,
Do things you rather doubt,
But ask me to start rhyming! -
Well, now, that's where I lose out.

But as I write the things I've said,
I stand here, mouth agape.
For from the words I've written
A verse has taken shape!

A CRY FROM MY HEART   Marilyn Scheibe

Our friendship, spotless and pure,
Would not, could not endure,
The deceptions, the falsehoods, the great conflagrations,
The wars, the fighting, the hatred of nations,
The strikes, the rumors, and the segregations.
For you, a fair white girl, and I, a Negress, couldn't dare
Try to face that awful stare,
From whites and Negroes, too,
When they saw that you liked me and I liked you.

Does color really matter so much?
Could you be blackened by my touch?

ONE SUMMER DAY   Marion V. Frahm

Today God crushed some yellow flowers
And sifted them in golden hours
Into the forest where they lay,
A lacework pattern on the clay.
A silence issued from the ground
And warmly wrapped itself around
The silken whisper of the trees,
Rustling in the elfin breeze
Which lightly gathered up the hours
And returned to God His crumbled flowers.
He tossed them then in sparks of light
Upon the velvet gown of night.

FIGURATIVELY SPEAKING   Margaret Berry

How my thoughts travel and wander
                from me!
Oh pen, help my writing -
                apostrophe.

My "thinker" is throbbing and threat'ning
Tarnation!
This tends to be
                alliteration.

My brain is a lion
That gives a great roar,
And scares off ideas and thoughts -
                metaphor.

This poem's terrific, superb -
You agree?
My modesty's baffling -
                hyperbole.

THE HIDDEN GOODNESS   Henry Hun Reynolds

Once in a great while
The Hidden Goodness that lies
Invisible within a man
          comes out
And shines brilliantly before the eyes
          of his comrades.
But then it again returns to the inner soul
And remains dormant for eternity,
          or until
once more it takes Courage and emerges,
driven out by circumstance.

PREJUDICE   Tanya Mortare

How can the decision you make be fair
If inside you know there's prejudice there?
If you accept only your own convictions,
Fair play is killed by false restrictions.

And if you think your race is far the best
And by way of giving the matter a test,
You say, "It's just because it's my race."
No other's can possibly win their case.

Take the religion for which you fight,
How can you know that it is right?
Hear what the others all have to say
And let each believe in whatever he may.

And even our country can only be best
If its honor stands above the rest.
Prejudiced opinions can never be kind,
So judge all things with an open mind.

BETWEEN ME   Pat Le Vere

Between me and the rising sun,
This way and that the cobwebs run;
Their myriad wavering lines of light
Dance up the hill and out of sight.

There is no land possesses half
So many lines of telegraph,
As those the spider-elves have spun
Between me and the rising sun.

WINTER WONDERLAND   Wilfred Faulkner

            The soft and velvet petals
Of that wondrous flower which grows,
Where heaven meets the clouds,
Are slowly, softly covering every bush and tree,
The field mouse slowly threads its tiny way
Amongst the downy flakes and seeks
The warmth of mate and brood,
The owl but ruffles feathers grey with age,
And looks without his lofty home,
He knows these fragile flakes will not long last,
And that again, some day, the earth will wake
            to spring's warm touch,
The furry cottontail contents itself with chewing
            on a tender root,
Not dreaming of the wonderful, yet deadly, menace
            of this white assassin.

I AM AMERICA   Michael Altschul

Do not fear;
I am not like your country -
I am America - free, not biased.

Huddle - Huddle at my bosom
and let me shelter you.

O, Boatman, Steer your boat directly
to these aboriginal shores from which
Gold does not spring, but
Liberty and Brotherhood.

Come to me, O Pioneers! O Refugees!
Warm yourselves with the common warmth of my Freedom,
lasting within my boundaries as long as I last -
and, I being God's Material Personification,
I shall last Eternally!

PRISON   Lois M. Girtz

Outside, the leaves whisper and chatter
like women, the blops of rain on the road
sound like children scampering -

Inside, the wind teases the curtain,
sucking it up to the screen for a wet kiss,
then releasing it with a flutter -

I sit with temples tingling,
            waiting, waiting,
The clock ticks,
            beating, beating ....

A WALLPAPERED LIFE — Mary Lucas

He repeats and repeats his routines,
His everyday doings like that of a wallpapered wall.
The same, the same, the same from day to day, week to week,
Never changing except for the collecting
Of dust and time.
The wallpaper will be cleaned, but time cannot repair it.
Man can be cleaned and time can repair.

NATURE'S SYMPHONY — Marilyn Peters

The wind begins the overture so mild
In tones like oboes whining through the quiet
And then the crickets start the melody
Accompanied by choruses of leaves
The theme in madness raises its clear notes
As bubbling streams rush madly o'er the rocks
And dash themselves until their waters great
Are rent, becoming single glistening drops.
Then comes the rain, like giant castanets,
That beats a rhythm suddenly profound
And makes the music raise its crying voice
And violently echo 'gainst the hills.
The clang of cymbals breaks into the song
As thunder raises high its lusty throat
And crashes forth in peals tremendously
Aquiver with the torment of a storm.
This symphony of nature is superb
More marvelous than any wrought by man
Because conducting this concerto great
Is God, the maestro of the elements.

INFINITY — Patricia Griffith

It is lonely here tonight.
The stars shine down -
Not friendly,
Not cold,
Just disinterested.
They were here
Long before I came,
And will remain
Long after I go.
People are born,
They live,
They die.
But the stars shine on,
Unaffected.

MY KINGDOM OF MAKE BELIEVE   Marilyn Grimes

I love to climb up in my tree,
And leave my troubles down below;
And play that the trees are greeting their queen,
As, in homage, they curtsy to and fro.

They shower me with their confetti of leaves,
And bow to show their allegiance to me,
As if I were an idol, and not
Just a make-believe princess enthroned in a tree.

DESPAIR   Myrna Garvey

Alone he stands, unnoticed and ignored
His eyes, the eyes of every man, so tortured
                        and afraid
The burden of life he carries himself
The weight too much to endure
His soul is leaden with heavy sacs
            of doubts and fears and mistrusts
For he has gone so far a distance
On the path that he has trod
That he no longer belongs to the world of
                        living dreams
Where the spirit is free and unafraid

THE CYCLE   Jane Davis

The spring of moods is hope renewed,
With darkness lifted from the day.
The restlessness, the wanderlust
Burst forth - the anemone - so gay.

The summer is our carefreeness
The heavy cloaks of winter shed.
The bright, long days of sunshine come;
Our hearts are gay; our sorrows dead.

Like fall, to each some sadness comes
A masquerade in colors riotous.
Soon trees are bare; the summer is gone.
We reminisce; our thoughts are pious.

Winter is the time of peace
A sheltered quietness regains
Our temperaments of seasons past
The king of moods - contentment - reigns.

A FRIEND   Shirley Lee Thompson

A friend is a person you can wholly trust,
You hardly can find one, but try you must.
A person who'll love you, and never be blue,
Over trifling things,
But rejoice with you,
In the happiness that friendship brings.

A friend is a person who'll laugh with you,
Over funny things that people do.
Who enjoys life and starts anew.
To enjoy life, and do those things
That mean so much to you.

FOOTPRINTS   Lilyanne Gregory

I watched from a window as he walked
Through the new-fallen snow,
Leaving his footprints, definite and distinct;
But like his soul, they seemed to have some direction -
Not vague, but exact and real.

My heart filled with happiness
And love for him who melted
The snow with his warmth and tenderness.

The footprints were soon covered
By fresh snow and steps of others,
But none will ever remain so vivid
In my memory as those that left
The picture of a soul
In the white snow.

THE SPACE TRAVELLER   George Nachwalter

Into outer space we move
At supersonic speed,
Breaking off our minute earth
As sound we do exceed.

The galaxies around our view,
Perhaps with earths their own,
Are spread throughout the universe
Some eons from our zone.

Dimensions more than those we have
Could very well exist
Perhaps outside infinity
Beyond our starry mist.

Yet no one knows what follows space,
Perhaps someday they'll find its place?

TO A NEON SIGN   Helen Campbell

Stars sparkle.
                    Wine, chandeliers and polished panes
All sparkle.
                    Drops of water, lakes of water, clear wines
                    and chandeliers
All sparkle.
                    Chinese sequins, dying fire, silvery sands
                    and diamonds
All sparkle.
                    Happy eyes sparkle, and I've even seen words
That sparkled.

INTERIM   Richard E. Nathan

It seems to all that Winter's gone.
    But yet he has not gone so far
That he might not return
    To give us more of what we spurn
Of cold and snowy weather.

The sun is neither hot nor cold;
    Spring is young,
And winter, old.
    But which is here
Cannot be told.

WINTER   Millard Howard

The color has gone from the gardens;
The grandeur has gone from the hills;
The winter has fallen upon us
With ices an d snows and with chills.

The lakes all are locked in their ices;
The meadows look barren and brown;
The trees stand like skeletal watchers
Receiving both country and town.

Before us a scene is unfolding -
A wilderness harsh and forlorn
With spectral bare bushes withstanding
The white drifted snow, as in scorn.

It fills us with sorrow and sadness.
We feel it with many a sting.
The earth in a climate of coldness
Is watching for beauteous spring.

PROGRESS   Ronald Strauss

No one stops the tide of progress
As it draws upon the beach of humanity,

No man is its conqueror
As it rushes forth in vanity,

Swallowing up all of man's great inspirations
With one significant thought in its great gulp;

To master all of man's achievements,
And to harness all the power of God.

GRIEF   Jean Spaulding

A tear
Upon a cheek
Will never mar the soul.
But grief too deep for tears will break
The heart.

THE SONG OF POSEIDON   Graham Cubberly

The calm is rent asunder
        as the storm begins to flail.
There's the rolling of the thunder
        and the slashing of the hail.
The wind begins to whistle
        and the waves begin to roar.
While the sea, a windblown missle,
        hurls itself against the shore.
A rolling ball of lightning
        is an eerie sheet of flame.
While the thunderbolt is calling
        the wind a martyr's game.
The tympani is thunder;
        the cymbals are the spray;
        the devil the conductor
        and the harp his lightning play.
The mountains of the oceans
        with their foaming snowing tops
        bow in maddening devotion
        to the wind that never stops.
And the shore's cold, bleak foreboding
        (of the high black promontory)
        is a trap of steel and cunning
        built to catch the fool, unwary
And the breaker's heavy booming,
        as it leaps upon the shore
        is a symbol of God's mending
        of our haughty human lore.

PAIN   Judy Atwood

Pain comes in waves;
First small ones, that grow and beat
Against your nerves, like waves against a rocky ledge
And knock you off your feet.
Then you walk farther on the roaring beach,
And keep on going deeper, deeper, into the black
                    waters of unconsciousness
Until you go down under, out of reach
Of any sunshine.

WIND BELLS   Carol Allen

Piquant music from the wind bells
Wafts into the air about me.
It mingles with the sweet illusions
Brought to my imagination by the wind.

My thoughts wander into distant places
Haunted by the far-off tinkling chimes.
They call me back from the horizon
Into a windswept and bleak reality.

TO A BROKEN WINDOW PANE   Jerry Raun

Once through thy crystal eyes
I viewed the outside world.
Parading clouds across the skies
Great pageants there unfurled.

But now thy face is shattered
By some object hurled thereon.
Thy views, distorted - scattered
Thy mirrored pictures, gone.

How like to life thy tragedy,
We have our hopes, our joy,
Until some force we cannot see
Comes surely to destroy.

But through each gaping hole
Still shines Thy light.
A beacon for the soul -
A candle in the night.

PAGLIACCI   Joan Bryning

Pagliacci! Oh, Pagliacci -
    You who suffered as I do,
Forced to hide sorrow, tears and anguish
    Behind a laughing face,
You know, for your love too, was made a mockery;
    Your dreams, your hopes - All -
All were shattered, as are mine,
    But we will go together - you and I,
Playing the clown without a care;
    And only the small, bitter, hysterical laugh
Will tell to someone wise enough to know
    That here are two broken hearts,
Two destroyed dreams - two lost loves.

TIME   Edna L. Morris

The sands of time flow thru the years and on;
All things are vanquished in its endless path.
Each evil deed you do ends; for anon
A new day starts which knows no wrong nor wrath.

These days are granted to you by the Lord;
Each has the privilege to live them through.
You ruin days which you cannot afford;
You are the one to blame and only you.

So make each day you live well worth the while,
And be your best to e v e r y o n e you see.
Return the frowns of others with a smile
And to great joy you soon will hold the key.

For time is short till death will take its toll,
And God will then possess your heart and soul.

MOMENTS OF FANCY   Wilma June Denman

These golden moments of fancy
When cares are aeons away
And one is engrossed in ecstasy
As the billowing breeze of the bay!

Ah! Were they only eternal -
To linger forever through life;
To gild with their silver halos
And own no sadness or strife.

Alas! Their richness too soon departs
Bringing us back to earth.
False wealth never knows real value,
But only a glittering worth.

I AM ALONE   Charlotte Hoagland

I am lost in the sadness of my heart,
   Enveloped in the inky blackness of my soul,
Carried along in this depth of ocean loneliness.
       I am alone!

Oh God! What is this thing which haunts me so?
   I do not know;
It follows me wherever I go, and blots out all my joy;
   I see this cloud of sadness which envelopes me like a fog.
       I am alone!

Far from the crowd around me, I am sealed in this prison
   of loneliness -
My soul cries aloud;
I yearn for peace -
       I am alone!

PANDORA   Sondra Taylor

Pandora's eyes are like sunflowers,
When she plays in the sun.
She uses her claws as plowers,
Her bark sounds like a gun,
Her tail wags like a fly-swatter.
Her feet look like an old ink blotter.
Her ears hang down kinda floppy-like,
And when she runs she looks like a bike,
Nevertheless, she pleases the family
And suits me to a "T."

FLAME   Charles A. Walworth

A tiny, nourished spark,
   Refulgency exudes
Which slowly climbing high
   In bashful, sulking moods,
Is sketched against the dark.

And now the flame begins
   Its fearful toll to take;
Fanned on by rising wind,
   Destruction in its wake,
It moves and cries and dins.

Though reaching toward the skies,
   Its fury's hottest blast
Straight 'gainst the earth is hurled
   'til worn and spent at last
It falters, droops and dies.

SPRING RAIN   Helen Marie Rittenhouse Johnson

The earth is like a lustrous woven cloth;
A background forms of muted grey and green,
And silver stripes of rain a pattern paint
On a tapestry that's lovely and serene.

A symphony in silver, green and grey,
For the long and flowing garment of the Earth;
And fasteners of golden daffodils
Complete the costume for her season of new birth.

THE FLOOD   LoAnna Holder

Cold death to the human heart;
    To spirits, gay revelry;
Horror to those who have lost
    Love in this make-believe sea.

Anguish to the broken ones;
    To the homeless, misery;
But this lake of hell to some
    Is heaven's delight to me.

EVENTIDE   Tommy Shelley

When day is o'er and eve is nigh,
The workman with one breath does sigh;
His work is done and rest remains
With peace of night to ease his pains.

When day is o'er and shadows fall
As hazy dreams to cloister all
In peace and rest till comes the morn,
On dusk our infinite trust is borne.

When day is o'er and birds at night
Do rest their weary wings from flight;
God's creatures all in night's repose
Their cares and trials darkness clothes.

When day is o'er and twilight deep
Surrounds the world in solemn sleep,
Come fading hours to soothe, to bless,
And eventide holds all in vast caress.

PEACE   Mary-Ellen Ringel

At last the day of great joy has arriv'n
The angels on a cloud of gold have come
My soul need not from its foul place be driv'n
It flies out to music by angels sung.

The great court is assembled there on high.
Defendants, sinners all, stand side by side.
A flourish of the trumpets fills the sky,
The music by angelic hosts supplied.

Is it to the great glory of the skies,
Or to the pit below that we are bound,
Accompanied by angels' symphonies
Or fawned upon by Hades' Hellis hound.

But justice reigns supreme for all around
My soul its sleep and peace at last has found.

PLUCKED FROM THE NIGHT   Mary Jane Hoffenden

I saw a meteor in the heavens
Shoot across the sky;
Swift flying as a plane,
But came not from it
Drone and sigh of engines.
Not a sound.
Just one illuminated line
To mark its route.
Even as from the sky,
God takes those beams of light,
So also shall He pluck us
One by one from Earth's dark night.

REMEMBERED SPRING   Mary Jean Aiken

The fragrance of frozen flowers,
The cold, cold fragrance,
Once warm and full
Of April,
Now cold with December,
Seeps in a crevice of torn memory and
Breaks the opening wider.

Remembered Spring seems long ago
And songs no longer soothe
The heart which holds a flower frozen -
A fragrance cold.

AUTUMN LEAVES   Charlotte R. Henry

Autumn leaves will start to fly,
When Mother Nature's breezes
Send them whirling through the sky,
To blow them as she pleases.

But when the wind begins to say,
"Old trees, you must not weep, "
We know it's time to turn away
And let the old leaves sleep.

APRIL SHOWERS   Carole Jeanne Baldwin

Something tapped at my window pane
Someone called me at the door
Someone laughed like a tinkling bell
The robin echoed it o'er and o'er.

I opened the door and window wide,
I felt the damp cool touch of rain
"Oh, were you expecting me, dear?
I am April Shower back again. "

MY PLACE IN THE FUTURE   Julia Bridge

The cloud that passes overhead
Is white and spotless pure,
I sit and wonder whence it came
And when 'twill meet the shore.

My future seems so like that cloud
Which floats so stately by
My place in life I haven't found
My dreams, I fear, will die.

But while my eyes do wander far
And gaze on heaven's friend,
I know that every human scar
Will help my ways to mend.

The place I find when time is due –
The plan of God 'twill be
The hour will come and then I'll do
The task mapped out for me.

THE NEW-BORN Patsy Carpenter

Oh, that he might have been blessed with birth
Into a world of tranquil love and peace,
That he might not be one of those who have
A simple part in life; a shortened lease.
He lies, a babe who's bathed in innocence,
He knows not what the future for him carries,
He is spared now of all the restless turmoil;
On the threshold of "Quiet Rest" he tarries.
I pray to God that one day very soon
This child may know a life of happiness,
That he may live without the threat of war,
A life of simple peace and tenderness.

PHOTOGRAPH Alberta Moellering

There sits your photograph.
It thrills me to look into the picture
At your eager, expressive face.
I can't stop a smile
From creeping up the corners of my mouth.
Now I feel the way it feels
To walk in an Autumn breeze.
Suddenly -
No memory brings back the way I felt
When near you; like running,
Face upturned,
In a quick torrent of mad spring rain.

Please -
If I can't run, heart pounding in Spring rain,
Let me walk, heart still beating,
In the Autumn breeze.

MY LOTUS LAND Carole Fern Hoover

I dream a dream of happiness,
Of sunny, sandy shores
Caressed by waves that toss about
And beat against my oars.
I'm lulled by never ceasing winds
That stir majestic trees,
And rush to blow away my cares
To whisper and to tease.
While now in perfect peace, I pray,
As gently rolls the mist,
That such a lovely paradise
Could just for me exist.

O, LOVE   Jacquelyn Culbertson

A silhouette I see, 'gainst the bleak, unbroken sky,
'Tis a tree, whose bare brown limbs look as
Melancholy as I.

I remember when only last summer or two
It stood leafy, so green, all ocvered in love,
Beneath a sky of blue.

Not too long ago I stood like that tree -
I stood wrapped in love, I stood shrouded in love -
Your love for me.

O' Love that has gone like the autumn leaves on wing,
Come back! O love, Dear love,
Come back with the Spring.

AGE   James Wolpman

Chant tattered black,
Shout wisps of grey,
Scream, scream furrowed flesh.
Let none thwart your din.
Chant and shout and scream:
"Antique!
Aged!
Senile!"

Gaze eyes, but gaze -
Enough.
Whisper never, whimper not.
Foul the word, pristine the emotion -
Aloof.
Only mirror, yes, reflect hopes and loves of men:
"Beauty!"

EMBARRASSED   Carole Dunham

The breeze is a thousand tornadoes
Blowing their furies at you
The voice of the world is mocking
Everything you do is wrong.
The rustle of trees is laughter
And everyone laughs at you.
Affairs are dropped for the moment
While everyone stares at you.
It always seems to go that way
When you've messed up your lines
In the Freshman Class play.

OF A ROLLICKING RIVULET   Gil Parker

It rambles and rumbles, as on and on it flows;
It hobbles and bobbles wherever it goes.
And it skips and slips and ripples and glides;
It runs in the open and then sneaks and hides.
It is shy and quite friendly, yet forceful and free;
It mirrors the twilight and outlines each tree.
It sparkles with moonlight and shines in the sun;
It cries in the shadows as its course must be run.
Then it sighs and it snickers and fades out of view,
Uncovering a pathway unfollowed and new.
But it keeps right on rambling and rumbling and flows
To wherever the water from little brooks goes.

THESE ARE POETRY   James Alpheus Butler

And these I know are poems real and true:
A heart that sings; a soul sincere; dim dawn;
A healthy mind; lush earth; the deep, clear blue
Of skies in spring; the sea; a verdant lawn;
A dream made real; bright colors; love, not hate;
A lithe, gay lass; good thoughts; the dearth of fear;
A blooming garden; flowers by a gate;
Deep words of wisdom by a saint or seer.

A little cottage where contentment dwells,
A limpid stream, so clear, so cool, so blue.
A hedge; a row of roses or bluebells;
A pansy cluster; goldenrods; the dew.
The charming words of friends; a magic wand;
May mornings; forests; friars, fairyland.

SPACE AND THE STAR   Jim Barthell

I flung a star to outer space
Then watched it as it soared - - -
Raced - - - slowed - - - seemed bored;
It soon began a crazy path
Like a madman's
Bent on plundering
To satisfy his wrath.
Then back to me it plummeted
With a scorching speed;
It crushed me, as a sinner
Would crush a mustard seed - - -
Who is to blame? Not I -
I think rather it was space
That caused my star to die.

I COME TO THEE   Dolores Chulick

Oh, come, my love, to where I wait for thee,
For swiftly falls the deep dark cloak of night,
The sun, a chariot, long hath left the lea,
And nothing shines now, save the stars' soft light.
Oh, come, my love; do heed my plaintive cry,
The earth is silent but for one sad song,
A night'ngale sings - "Oh! Come, or I shall die" -
And my poor heart joins his, ay! twice as strong.

I realize that now my call's too late,
The warm, dark earth will soon enclose you, dear.
A life alone is not to be my fate;
My last life's word is true; I'll shed no tear:
You'll need not, e'er again, to come to me,
For now, my love, my heart, I come to thee.

UNIVERSITY OF WASHINGTON   Lucetta Nace

Sweet muse, of the far ranges,
Thy kindness is overshadowed
            by unspeakable distances;
Yet some have glimpsed your
            thin veil
In the fog-gloomed shadows.
Open-eyed wonder and sad love,
Questions, and rules of abandonment,
Methods and rebellions
Bespeak a path to your heights . . .
Though how false, how false
            this all becomes;
No path leads to your regions,
But you have been seen, you have been seen,
            you have been seen!

HATE   Arline Robbins

Hate, like a volcano,
Lies quietly smoldering;
Then suddenly without warning,
It bursts forth with a thunderous roar
To spill forth the hot lava of destruction.

Hate, like a volcano,
Heaps misery and devastation
Onto everything in its path,
And from the volcano of Hate
Pours forth the ruination of humanity.

TO CAESAR   Jetta M. Fucito

Did Caesar have to be so great and conquer all of Gaul?
Why did he have to be the Ruler of Rome at all?
Couldn't he have been a simple man just like you or me?
No, he had to be a famous one - go down in history!

He's bad enough in English class - Literature and such,
But when meeting him in Latin - that really is too much!
If Caesar only knew just how we struggle and we slave,
There might be a possibility, he'd turn over in his grave.

Pupils do dislike him • I feel sorry for the man,
'Cause all he did was live a life as anybody can.
Could it be we're jealous of his glory and his fame?
Could it be we would like to play his very daring game?

We lack the strong ambition, the kind that Caesar had,
In truth, we sure envy him and that's what makes it sad.
That's why Brutus killed him - oh, what jealousy can do!
And that's why we dislike him - if Caesar only knew!

So don't turn your backs on Caesar, bear with him, please do,
And on completion of your studying, you'll find this to be true:
You will give a cheer for Caesar - to Caesar Hip - Hurray!
Hurray! 'Tis the end of Caesar - throw that book away!

AN ENIGMA   Barry Traub

Is love a panacea, or another false illusion,
Which comes quickly towards us from the ocean,
And like the fog, disappears again towards the sea?
Is love divine and true, or is it merely physical ecstacy?
Oh, God above, please answer me.

LIFE   Shirley Butler

Life is like a rippling brook.
    It flows forever on.
The waters ever wandering
    Like a carefree vagabond.

Life is like an apple tree,
    Which blossoms in the spring.
The fragrance of its petals
    Makes children dance and sing.

Life is like a rose that blooms
    In beauty with the years.
The raindrops on its petals
    Are gleaming human tears.

THE BUTTE   Ethel Terwilleger

Here at thy feet, majestic Butte, I stand,
What helping advice wouldst thou give me?
Oh, Thou with stately mountain pillars grand
With thy council wise still I would agree.
From the long reign of thy exalted throne
And with thy rugged countenance time stained
Most wise and all discerning thou hast grown
What is best of the knowledge thou hast gained?
A firm foundation thou wouldst have me build
Where by thy toil my life I must conduct;
So that it with honor may be filled.
A mansion of my self I will construct
That I may stand erect like thee with grace
And gaze at all the world with honest face.

TO MUSIC   Nancy Johnson

O! Chalice of celestial treasury,
O! Nectar sacred to the lips of kings
That mortals taste and on ethereal wings
Soar high to heaven's gates in ecstasy,
To thy sweet rapture let my spirit flee.
The mighty stream, the flower, the small bird sings,
The majesty of lake and mountain rings
In ears, the tainted hosts of purity.
Through eyes the spacious world may not behold,
Nor tongue its pleasure voice in eloquence,
Yet each may trod where paths of mystics wend.
For those whom years have destined to be old,
And those attired in youthful innocence,
May each list to, yet ne'er thee comprehend.

REALITY   Doris Jeanne Rhule

The weary soldier knelt alone,
Beside his comrade fair.
The rain glistened on his cheek
And fell upon his hair.

"Oh God, " he prayed while looking down
Upon the cold, still face,
"Halt the wars, cease the shot,
All terror, please erase. "

And then the prayer was ended.
Once more he marched along.
Gone were his youthful dreams
Gone - the triumph from his song.

A WINTER DAY   Virginia Curtis

The sky, so overcast with gray
Reflects in mood the winter day.
The rain has not begun to fall
Upon the turf. The mournful call
Of birds is faint and far away.

Sentinel pine, a mighty tower
Silently guards the bush and bower.
Searching for food, a dirty cur
Shakes the water from his fur
On daffodils, gay notes in flower.

UNTO THE LIGHT   Doris Langford

Familiar are the eyes of darkness,
That steal from hidden places
Unto the light of night
And resume their chosen places
In the grandeur of fallen skies.

Familiar, too, the pulse of time
That runs with flowing traces
Into the minds of men
And leaves great cherished faces
In death upon the rotted earth.

A STORM   Barbara Frances Gould

Black clouds covering up the blue.
Air is still and dry to you.
A storm is coming.

Seagulls leave the open spaces.
Toward the land they turn their faces.
A storm is coming.

Heavens open and rain comes down,
Filling the lakes and soaking the ground.
The storm is here.

Bits of blue peep through the gray.
The sun comes out but does not stay.
The storm is passing.

In the sky a rainbow bright
Shows to all the Creator's might
The storm is over.

TOP FLOOR . . . EAST WINDOW   Nancy White

Ivy leaves touching the window . . .
Gray ghostlike fog shading the light within . . .
Panes of glass with their smudged and broken particles . . .
All seem like a mirrored light upon life's drear and drudgery.
No bright laugh penetrates the broken panes . . .
A nooselike twine ever ready for mankind's breath.
And the ivy, so natural with clawing fingers of despair
Wrapped around our hearts.
A gravely paneled staircase,
Gray in the humid fog
Points to a desperate flight upward without ever an end.

But no . . .
The window is but in need of scrub,
The ivy of trim,
The dream in need of forgetting.

A GENERAL, TO A DEAD PRIVATE   Dean Koolbeck

Do not look at me, soldier --
Your eyes that never will close
Have in them questions that I cannot answer.

Do not frown at me, soldier -
The blood on your forehead
Stains my hands, who ordered you to die.

Do not stare at me, soldier -
Silent hatred of the dead
Is too great a load for man to bear,
And many have died today.

CYCLE   Ann E. Smith

The last leaf is gone.
The grass, green before,
Is fading,
As the rest of the earth,
Into a colorless, cold, still picture.

Silently, slowly, in the dusk,
A light snowflake falls.
Then more and more until
Heaven, opening her heart,
Makes the picture, once drab,
A living, crystal scene.
The cycle is made.

THE ONES I HATE   Richard Gregory

My life is like a tarnished spoon,
And I am lonely and sad indeed,
My heart is a lone wolf baying at the moon,
As I wonder when you'll be free from hate and greed.

I have no past to look back to,
My present is very lonely and sad,
You think you've triumped over me too,
But you will learn; and I'll be glad.

I have no future to look for,
You saw to it that I would not.
Your face is like an ugly scar
Upon my life; I hope you'll rot.

Your life is like a tapestry - rent and torn,
Your motives are black with hate,
You're full of lies and hate and scorn,
Someday I know you'll meet your fate!

HONESTY   Lois Webb

An old-fashioned virtue, honesty
Important in our daily lives
Is a better means of protection
Than any number of knives.

This virtue is acquired, not inherited
By memory of some teaching
You have it or not, for with honesty
There can be no reaching.

THE WEEPING WILLOW   Therold Ellis Krammes

There's a tree in the meadow,
But it's not the tree you think.
It is the weeping willow,
Sighing by the brink.

It bends its boughs with every wind;
Its rustling leaves seem to say,
"What a wonderful world to live in,
On such a beautiful day!"

And so the willow weeps all day,
By the waters which flow so free.
She is only singing in her natural way,
Sighing for joy, you see.

BEHIND CLOSED DOORS   Jan Williams

"My doors are closed.
Closed to those who think differently from me.
I have barred the doors
And thrown away the key.
"Stay out, " says a sign hung high above the knocker.
"Stay out and this means you. "
It means you who have a different religion than I have.
It means you who are of a different coloring or race from mine.
"Stay out" you who disagree with me,
Because I am more intelligent and have a higher mode of life than you. "
This is the statement of the intolerant.
They live for themselves,
And live within themselves.
America unite!
Open your arms to the people beyond the sea,
Be they white, black, or Oriental.
Open your hearts
And come out from behind the closed doors.

AMERICA   Jane Lueck

I saw the broad, level, endless plains,
And the waves of green and gold;
I saw the mountains, guardians of beauty,
Erect and regal like kings of old;
I saw the valleys, the deserts, and the forests,
The turbulent rivers, lakes and streams;
I saw the people of every race and creed
Working, playing, and sharing dreams;
And suddenly I knew that this was a precious land,
A land of peace and beauty, of freedom, hope and love.
O America! May you never cease to be
A land of stalwart principles and a guiding light to me!

DAWN   Nancy Marie Conrad

The morning light now breaking
Drives the night a-far.
The little sunbeams waking
Sing lullabys to the morning star,
And set the dewdrops shimmering
Wherever cobwebs are.
Now a robin singing
Calls its mate to say
That every soft wind sighing
Wakes the flowers of May.
The world is roused from dreaming
To greet the dawn of day.

GRIEF   Rodger Robinson

Parterres of purple and magenta tulips,
Delicate lacy saffron, and ice blue iris,
Waving, upward striving spears of canescent lilies,
Ochre daffodils, zinc white callas, and scarlet crocus
Decorate my beautiful garden.

I ignore all but the bleeding hearts,
And I lie beneath them
My tears nurturing their growth.

                        Patty Muretic

        A mother is like a clock.
        She knows the time, by instinct
        To eat or put little ones to bed,
        Or how much time tonight for a story to be read.

        She knows how many seconds will lapse
        Between a fall and the cry for mercurechrome,
        She knows if Daddy will be late or not;
        If so, she keeps his supper hot.

        Mothers know lots of other things:
        How to paint, and sing songs, and sew,
        Or soothing hurt feelings, she knows what to say
        And how to keep children happy on a rainy day.

        There's only two things that mothers d o n ' t know;
        When to stop loving a naughty daughter or son,
        Or when to stop working
        When her day s h o u l d be done.

                    CLOCKS   Betty Edney

        "Know thyself, "
        Said Socrates.
        His words are composed
        Of wisdom.
        But when have I time
        To learn of myself,
        With clocks ticking time,
        Always, always,
        Before my eyes?

WHERE RAIN ONCE LAY   Bill Nethercut

The day is dreary, bleak and dark
Trees, standing in the park,
Appear to be
Gaunt and spectral things.

The low moan and the ceaseless wind
Are quiet at times
And then again
Relentless in their fury.

Ice figures form on window sills
Where rain once lay . . . .
Before the cold wind came.

BACKYARD   Dick Hemsted

The hyacinths have pushed their way
Through loamy soil to meet the day.
Some tulips budding one by one
Are out to greet the warm spring sun.
The lilacs with their quiv'ring leaves
Perfume the air, and in the eaves
A robin builds its nest of string
And sticks, and then begins to sing
His song of joy and happiness.
The wind is like a warm caress
That seems to gladden heart and mind
And when it passes, leaves behind
A sense of quiet solitude.

DANCE!   Nancy Beardsley Stiles

The music races through my veins.
I am as one possessed.
My soul blends with vibrant tones.
My body sways;
I dance.

I see no thing; I hear no thing;
From violins' soaring heights,
Foamy clouds I search - and
Crouch in valleys of despair
To muted tones of saxophones;
And make a startled, quick retreat
As sinister drums beat soft and sweet.
The music ends.

My soul is drained.
No longer can I dance.

EVENING CONTEMPLATION   Margarita Shaup

The breezes sigh and laughingly retire,
Trees are whispering as they settle for the night;
Voices of the birds are murmuring words of wonder,
And dusk's dark curls are freely pinned with stars.

The evening is mysterious and holy,
Secrets that it hides defy interpretation;
In the peaceful quiet, never truly silent,
My soul perceives the presence of the Lord.

CLOUDS   Mary Ann Storrs

Flowing clouds are changing
        optical reflexes;
Their fluffy pattern changes
        to some may cause perplexes.
Clouds mold and fall away alone;
        they gather to form a sifted dome.
Birds find their flight an endless
        journey,
The heavens an eternal sovereignty.

THE RAIN   Betty Jean Alligood

The night is long and dreary still
The rain pours slowly down;
It beats upon the window sill;
It makes a wearisome sound.

There is no star in the sky tonight;
There is no moon to shine;
The rain has taken from our sight
The things we've kept in mind.

The rain begins to pour so hard;
The night grows gloomy and dim;
The shadows creep upon the yard
The night has lost its rim.

Then day begins to come at last;
The sunshine is so bright;
It throws to us a long, bright cast;
The rain is out of sight.

LAUGHTER   Marilyn Smith

Gentle, rippling, rising laughter
   At some fanciful delight,
Soft and quiet, inward laughter,
   More a state of bliss than might;

Loud, jovial, buoyant laughter,
   As if, being long confined,
Is released with sudden fullness
   Glad to drop its air resigned.

For laughter is ever-changing,
   Different tones and different shades;
Though it encircles a world so troubled,
   Yet it rises . . . never fades.

THE SAN JACINTO MONUMENT
                    Patricia Hampton Noland

A creamy, slim monument, crowned with a star,
Reflected full length in a pool;
A brilliant example outlined in the sky
Of God using man as His tool.

Dignified shaft, loved by all native sons,
Symbolic of freedom we've won;
In memory of heroes who died in that war,
Our tribute to deeds which they've done.

Tall, serene sentinel, watching o'er all,
You're seen and admired from afar,
Proudly, aloofly looking down at the world,
Nothing your calm beauty can mar.

WINTER TREE   Terrell Jordan

Winter tree, do you have sorrow
For your leaves which have been taken?
I say unto you cry not, no,
Not for what is gone, but
Look you, what you have now, beauty
In the outline of your many
Arms so varied, framing velvet
Blue in many shapes and forms,
Designs excelled not by the rosebush,
Clinging to the ground with coldness.
She has not the stately looks that
You display so proudly, vainly.
What you have not think not on,
But of what you have, be thankful.

THE ETERNAL SEA   Mary Frances Page

Through all the years of ancient history,
The sea has washed the sands both day and night.
It sweeps the crags and ships that sank at sea,
It cleanses minds of men and makes them right.
The mighty sea is powerful and strong,
And yet it can be peaceful, gentle, too.
The wind at sea will always sing its song
Of mighty tempest or of sea gulls' mew.
The sea could give you wise philosophy
It gleaned from men of wisdom long ago.
It makes you want to live and breathe as free
As it has been and shall forever flow.
    And in your heart it makes you want to be
    As wise and strong and mighty as the sea.

ETHEREALITY   Colleen Wright

Strange tapestry of life we rudely weave;
Each heartbeat, breath, and step, a tainted thread
Encumbered in time's quick momentous stead.
The pattern of a dream, which some perceive
To be inane; a thought of make-believe,
Proves sweeter far in color than in tread
Of all men's glory lying past, and dead.
T's quality of thought to which we cleave.

Could we but reach those rigid cliffs of time,
And bind those myriads of future hours;
Then would we weave a cloth with scene benign;
A portrait of the soul; its earthly flowers
Of thought and deed shorn of iniquity;
A picture, framed by that which is to be.

DISHWASHING   Doris DeVore

Dishwashing - task I used to dread,
But now I've come to love instead,
The warm, soft suds upon my hands
The pleasant clatter of the pans.

And when I'm finished then I view:
Sparkling glasses, china, too.
Silver resting in its chest.
(This I like to wash the best.)

Then supper comes; and when it's through,
There'll be more dishes left to do.
So - since it is an endless task,
Why not enjoy it? - This I ask.

SONNET FROM THE TOILER   Delmo Maurer

To be free as the happy lark, away
From all this toil. The cares, the sorrow, and
The troubles keep me away from vain play.
To be free as the happy lark, so grand.
Is there no joy, relief, escape which was
To be enjoyed on earth? What turn from toil
Can I, a toiler, take? This problem does
Appear as dark as any sea of oil.
But then the answer slowly dawns. It states
A faith unconquerable, a faith for me
And all mankind. It gives this word which rates
Most high: "Come unto me; there's rest for thee. "
The toil of life is comet-like; it's here
And gone. The answer is the Saviour dear.

OCTOBER   Susanne Raines

October is the scent of singeing leaves,
The new-born crispness of the tangy air,
The staccato laughter of rollicking children,
The driving animation of inspired youth.

October is the dying of a quiet summer,
The wistful turn of changing seasons,
The mingling of the old life with the new,
The coming of the unforeseen future.

October is the glowing loveliness of life,
With scarlet hue and flaming torch,
It is another bright horizon,
Of our never-ending world.

THE PALM TREES   Marie Baldridge

The palm trees sigh, as if content,
Grateful for the storm's release,
They appear settled, as if
They have, at last, found peace.

The hurricanes once attacked these palms
With lashing winds and rain,
But even after such turmoil and stress
These palms found peace again.

Now, when the world is torn by war,
And the quest for peace seems vain,
Remember, that like the wind-driven palms,
The world, too, may find peace again.

THE BEAUTY OF DEATH   Richard Mertens

When I behold the summer's changing scene
As autumn overpowers her in his sway,
I see the lofty boughs expel their green
And deck themselves in splendorous array
Of blazing yellows and majestic red
Commixed with russet and with somber browns,
And when I view the vales and hills outspread
Enclad and tipped with golden robes and crowns
And see above each leaf-filled forest lane
The trees their bright-hued arches interblend,
I know that summer will not fall in vain,
For glory will be hers until the end.
Her death is one not sorrowful but grand,
She dies by spreading beauty through the land.

THE RESURRECTION   Paul V. Orlett

Against the sullen sky a barren tree,
A skeleton of winter's fiercest gale,
Now breaks its weary boughs with ice impaled,
Its branches dark with death for all to see.
Beneath, the ground has swallowed summer's glee,
And flowers have deserted every vale,
The air is cold; there sounds a mournful wail,
The birds, the merciless Wind, and her knife, flee.

Then comes the Resurrection; Life appears,
The earth reopens; plants seek out the sun,
The sky is bright, the bird no longer fears,
Red buds spring forth; and God's spring work's begun:
The well-dressed trees bring God to us so near,
To view His great and gorgeous beauty come.

INSPIRATIONS   Reginald M. S. Bjornstad

Come they do, come they will,
Be they through, not until,

Ink upon the white,
Man, mind and might,

Looking upon the dead,
Nothing new to be said,

Same said, same come they will,
Never through, end of time until,

Thoughts of my dear, I write,
Pen and ink and candlelight.

WE MUST GO   Ray McKinley Peters

When death comes stealing upon you and me
My dear, we shall not be afraid to go;
For Christ came down to die for me and thee
To take us up with him from here below.
For this blest reason we shall have no fears
Of parting from this vain world where we dwell.
If one should go, then we shall shed no tears,
For deep inside the breast our hearts will swell
With joy and longing then to take our place
Beside each other at our Lord's own feet.
In Heav'n we shall partake the Master's grace,
And there shall share the Love of Christ replete.
If we our lives like Christ do fashion, death
Holds no dismay when we draw that last breath.

WHY WERE YOU BORN?   Leora Houston

Did heaven send you to this speeding sphere
To fight against the nations of the world,
To struggle for your life's blood, to be hurled
Against relentless rocks of human fear,
Want, need, and ignorance? Is it your fate
To be exalted over common men?
Do crowns or chains control your musings when
In silent solitude you meditate?

Why, you were born to mingle with the wise
On earth; to live a day of loveliness
Whose morning, noon, and night a song should be.
The hope of ages should shine in your eyes.
Your hand in mine, we'll walk in happiness
With faith undying through eternity.

DREAMING   Eileen Dawson

Yesterday morning you dreamed of last night,
And last night you dreamed of today;
Today you dream of tomorrow,
But not a minute will stay.

In March you dream of fair April,
In April of sweet, lovely May;
Sweethearts in May dream of June-brides,
Seems we dream all our minutes away.

In winter we dream of fair summer,
In summer we dream of the fall;
If seems that of all our professions,
We are dreamers more than all.

PHILOSOPHY   Lenore MacGaffey

As surely as the silver dawn dispels the dreaming night,
As gladly as the grateful birds awake to greet the light,
As radiant as the rising sun, as fresh as fallen dew;
So, beautiful with brightest hope, life laughs and loves anew.

When budding flowers have blossomed fair, and faded petals fall,
When sun has seen its zenith and its royal splendours pall,
When sweetest songs of early hours sink to a murmured sigh,
When life has lost its zest and Time has severed every tie;

Then,
As glorious gleams the setting sun and slowly fades away,
As evening comes, celestial cloud, to dim the light of day,
As dusk distils its hazy hues and mists of dreaminess;
So, softly, gently, lover-like - sweet comes the call of death.

EUCALYPTUS TREE   Barbara Stinchcomb

Graceful, tall and evergreen
With branches reaching high,
There stands the eucalyptus tree
Outlined against the sky.

Its drooping tendrils bow and sway
With every summer breeze,
And seem to send out greetings gay
To all the other trees.

When banks of fog might cloud the skies
It stands like sentinel bold
Until the morning sun shall rise
And turn its leaves to gold.

A LOST SOUL   Marthanne Bauknight

Condemned is the man that knows not God,
But is consumed by earthly deeds,
And walks the path that Christ once trod
To plant therein his sinful seeds;

Who lives and dwells here on God's earth
Guarded by Him from fear and pain;
Who breathes God's breath with endless girth,
Yet uses His precious name in vain.

He's much too blind to see the strife,
Which his unrighteous life will bring,
And comes to realize too late
That torment follows death's cold sting.

DESOLATION   George W. Wilson

Dry, arid winds sweep the lonely waste,
Drifting sands enshroud the dismal scene
Here life's symbols quickly are erased.
Here the sight where man, the proud, has been.

A jagged rock, a piece of metal worn
Reach up above the sands, soon to disappear.
A wooden hut, cracked and dry and torn
Lies half submerged, its surface thin and sere.

A choking cloud blots the view, then clears,
And lo! naught disturbs the surface of the plain.
The swirling , shifting sea of sand appears,
And man, the proud, once more has built in vain.

A GIFT   Thea Reber

When in the lovely hours of Spring we sit,
And wonder what has made the flowers so rare,
The artist seemed to know just where to fit
Each little blossom in its place with care.

The soft and soothing breeze from far up high
Descends upon us just to keep things cool.
It seems that we can only sit and sigh,
At wonders that He made without a tool.

Along with spring there comes a fancy true
Which makes each one of us seem to forget
And loose those frowns which tell we've had the blues
And gain great interest in the folks we've met.

God made the world for us, I have belief,
Just so that we could loose all of our grief.

FREEDOM   Colleen Hayes

There is freedom in this country;
Is there freedom in our souls?
Are we pushed and shoved about by men,
Without some worthy goals?

There is freedom in this country ;
Is there freedom in our minds?
Are our words and actions chained by fear,
Or hate of kindred kinds?

There is freedom in America,
A freedom that won't part,
A freedom worth all fighting for;
Is there freedom in y o u r heart?

LADY OF SPRING   Janice Kaltriter

Now enters the beautiful Lady of Spring,
    Spring rains in her face, and March winds in her hair,
A necklace of raindrops, a gown of sky blue,
    A magnificent wardrobe, so fresh and so new.

Still defying the sun, lies black snow on her breast,
    Though unsightly to see - matters little to me,
For 'neath it I'll spy tiny greens peeping soon,
    Their burden of buds making ready to bloom.

Last traces of winter are melting away,
    The hurrying streams rush to welcome her too.
And an army of robins comes into my view,
    As the Lady of Springtime begins her debut.

NIGHT REVERIE   Jean Marie Edge

I like to walk on moonlight nights
    Under the velvet sky,
While stars above with their lustrous lights
    Glisten, the moon to defy.

I watch my shadow grow and shrink
    In the gleam of the corner light,
Which guides the ones who pass, a link
    To the known from the unknown night.

I like to approach the house I call home,
    Which glows with goodness and love,
The place to return for one who would roam,
    A refuge on earth as Above.

DESTINY   Herbert Prochnow

Life walks hand in hand with Fate
Upon each misty, quiet night;
They choose Fame's sparkling sentinels
And place them on some lofty height.

Men wander on in aimless search
To find the glory of renown;
They must dream and pray and hope
That they can grasp the mystic crown.

Some learn the aureole of Fame
And from the heights draw noble breath.
Yet all are claimed by Fate and Life
And by the Nothingness of Death.

TO SEPTEMBER   Sandra E. Flood

Ah, September! Fleeting month
Drowsing in late sunshine's beams,
Yours is the bustling stir of autumn,
Drenched in summer's hazy dreams.

Your fields sprout shining goldenrod,
And golden are your cloudless skies;
Your hills are gowned in royal purple;
Oh stay, before your splendor dies!

For swifter flow your rivers, much
More swiftly than they flowed before . . . .
We call, "Adieu!" We watch you dying;
Sinking to the forest floor.

THE PATHS OF TIME   Amy Schoonover

Whenever I walk in a dusty street
The constant rhythm of my feet
Seems with its crushing sound to say,
"I wonder how many have passed this way?"

And when I traverse a sidewalk wide
I think of the history it might hide;
I say to myself, "How many today
Think that once this was a forest way?"

And the paths I tread seem to say to me,
Many a soul has passed here. See
The marks of many a weary load
That was carried once down this ancient road!"

THE MAGIC OF AUTUMN   Avon Peterson

Sporting tang and crispness proudly,
The autumn air becomes a breeze.
Sometimes rattling the windows loudly . . . .
Shaking bright leaves from the trees.

The rich green grass has changed its hue,
With autumn dress a shade of brown.
Bright summer flowers have faded too;
The smoke of leaves covers the town.

The pantry shelves are amply filled
With fruits of spring and summer's labor,
And now that summer's voice is stilled,
Winter then becomes our neighbor.

TO THE FIRE IN MY HEARTH   Bruce C. Duff

O roaring fire, killer of the cold,
Set high your flames and blaze with all your might
And let me feel the warmness that you give
From out the hearth, this snowy, frozen night.
For I am old and weary, and do know
That on a night like this the wind can blow
'Till I conceive my courage shall not live.
Then, through the window, Death will slowly creep
And cross the floor, yet making not a sound;
But hover o'er me when my bed he's found.
So blaze you high and crackle with delight,
And chase the frozen air into the night.
Or else, O fire, killer of the cold,
I shall lie back and feel the weight of sleep.

SPRING   Katherine Kittle

Naughty March comes blustering in,
Lamb's meekness o'er lion's wrath does win
And fills the air with earthy smell
As Spring awakes each hill and dell.

Soon April approaches, sweet and mild,
And how happy is the child!
Frequent are the peaceful showers,
Leaving rainbows and later flowers.

Then comes the merry month of May,
Bringing cheer throughout each day.
Fields and woodlands robed in green
Awe us all as they are seen.

These are the months of Spring's sweet reign,
Proving that hope is not in vain.

THE DREAMER   Nelda LeBleu

While others worked and slaved away
    He rested in the sun all day.
He thought them slaves of time's drear mood
    To have to toil for daily food.

He had no foe or worldly care
    Till winter laid the fields all bare.
He shivered as he cut his wood
    And got along as best he could.

The soft snow clothed the earth in white
    The moon arose in golden light
He forgot hunger and duty
    This dreamer saw only beauty.

MEMORIES   Amanda Klemme

These thoughts are rare, to them I'll always cling
Sweet memories of childhood on the farm:
The orchard trees and the old grapevine swing,
The hide and seek in the big musty barn,
The smell of dark damp earth just freshly plowed,
The shocks of grain, the cricket's chirping sound,
An April shower, blue skies, a fleecy cloud,
A pheasant call from distant meadow ground,
The old steam engine and the harvest crew,
The fun of sliding down the new straw stack,
Wild prairie flowers rich in morning dew,
Ripe strawberries along the railroad track,
And I, light heart, with not a care to hide,
Barefoot with Rover trotting at my side.

THE LAND I LOVE BEST   Jo Ann Dunlop

Here I've lived and here I'll die
And lie on the plains where the birds fly by;
Where the animals roam and the grass waves free,
And the stars in the sky shine as bright as can be;
Where the hush of night in its mellow stillness
Breathes a fragrance rare with a delicate faintness,
And all living things repose for a while,
While old Mr. Moon looks down with a smile.
He sees Mother Earth cradled in sleep;
Just like a sentinal, he watches his sheep,
Till the dawn comes creeping, lighting the sky,
Waking the new day with a welcome cry.
So let me lie way out here in the west,
Slumbering on in the land I love the best.

THE HEALING BALM   Barbara Ellis

The church was empty, save for me,
I knelt in silent reverie,
Alone with Him, my God and King
To Whom all creatures praises sing.

I felt His presence all about,
And, in my heart, there was no doubt
That He would rid me of my fears
And gently brush away the tears.

And so I opened wide my heart
And to Him did my grief impart;
He heard His child's mournful cry
And to my aid did swiftly fly.

MY PRAYER   Jeanette Juric

Christ, Everloving, have mercy on me,
Teach me to love and to serve only Thee.
Make me obedient, respectful and kind,
With links of love bind my heart to Thine.
When signs of temptations about me do band,
Wipe them away with a move of Thy hand.
Ask Mary Immaculate, Thy Mother most pure,
For disease of the soul, to give me a cure.
Beg her to love me though hard it may be,
I put You to death, yet You gave her to me.
My heart cries out with a longing plea,
My Jesus, my Jesus, Forsake Thou not me!
His answer comes clear as the evening tide:
"Why weepest thou, child? I am here at thy side. "

REFLECTIONS   Sara Lou Teets

Ah sweet life and death!
I would I had the view
That mystic nature saith
To all and not a few.
Like a new shining star we appear
With the eagerness and radiance of youth,
Bravely overcoming our doubts and fears,
Yet always searching for the path of truth.
As dawn takes the place of night,
God's star never seems to lose its course;
Yet we seem afraid of death's forewarning light,
As we have lost the important driving force.
But the star fades away without a sigh,
As it knows it will be welcomed on high.

TWILIGHT'S SONG   Verna Angela (Sandy) Fletcher

The days are long
As the darkness falls;
I hear the song
That the twilight calls.

The song with soft
And mellow notes
Which are carried aloft
Upon wings, and float.

For a moment all is still,
With shadows falling upon the hill;
Its melody flowing forever o'er
As it seemed to fall the night before.

A BOY'S LIFE   Barbara Hight

Give me my arrow and bow so strong
            Give me the hills, the trees, and the lawn.
            This is what every boy of age needs
            To play Indians and cowboys, and yell "Yippee."
            To be on a farm and to be free,
            This is a boy's life, a life for me.

            My mother is busy - too busy to see,
            I need no toys, except the hills and the trees.
            She buys me things,such pretty things,
            But I care not for these.

            I love to ride and to sing
But most of all, I love these things.
My arrow, my bow so strong, the hills,
The trees, the meadows and lawns.

A VALENTINE TO MY PARENTS   Ann Therese Manzo

    It was a starry night, last night,
        And all of Heaven shone;
    I looked about the Heavenly bliss,
        For I was all alone.

    I had a word or two, I guess,
        With my bright star above
    And we decided truthfully
        That you are whom we love.

    And so because of this fair day,
        When thoughts are so sublime,
    I now would like to ask you two
        To be my Valentine.

DIRGE   Andy Oberhofer

    The moon rose round and golden
    On the crisp, chill night.
    The leaves were poems of color
    From the north wind's bite.

    Sharp on the night's cold stillness
    Came the baying of a hound,
    The funeral dirge of summer,
    This wailing, dismal sound.

    A ghost ride high against the moon -
    I watched its eerie flight,
    As the soul of the summer went winging
    Afar through the chilly night.

THE OCEAN   Phyllis Emory

The ocean's a serpent - churning, tossing,
Spreading over victims its watery fingers;
Wildly beating the ships which are crossing.
After the angry wave, the white foam lingers,
Giving the ocean a touch of white magic.
Beneath, lies the power of life or death,
Which - to many sea-lovers is tragic;
The cry to the ocean, the last word on their breath.
The lovers of the sea know another story.
The serenity and calm after the storm.
Reveal the ocean in its majestic glory.
And again to the ocean their hearts grow warm.
Of the ocean, some recall life's tragedy;
While others see only God's majesty.

MORNING   June Nixon

Tremulous whistles announce its arrival.
Startled, the city awakens in fear.
Soothing and peaceful the sun like a mother
Croons, "Sleeping children, the morning is here."

Running away, like the devil from beauty,
Street girls flee back to their haunts out of sight;
Humble and poor, an old lady kneels upright,
"Greetings, my Jesus, my true God of Light."

Happy or bitter, the sun shines on all,
Bringing us hope or the depths of despair;
How we accept it is our special choice,
Joy comes, however, to God's blest and fair.

SEPTEMBER LEAF   Christine Brown

You dance so lightly through the air.
You flutter at a thunder.
You drift by branches, high and wide
And gaze at them in wonder.

You tease the Autumn wind and then,
As he awakens slyly,
You rush behind the nearest tree
And peek out at him shyly.

He tumbles you quite gently on.
You reach to touch a flower
And then you nestle on the ground
For a warm September shower.

NATURE Joan Sudolski

The autumn leaves fall, the trees grow bare;
Beauty has left nature, everywhere.
The cleansing raindrops wash the earth,
Preparing the world for a shining rebirth.
The days are gray, the nights are cold,
The sun has lost its shining gold -
Nature has closed its eyes to rest.

The trees blossom out, the flowers drip with dew,
Beauty has returned, the skies are bright and blue.
The earth is clean, the air is sweet -
God has made nature tidy and neat.
The days have been mellowed, the nights are made warm -
Nature has awakened, a new world is born.

A PRISON Jean Finnemore

As I lift my eyes fringed with lacework brown
I see day breaking in the east, so meek
The bright sunlight then fills my room so bleak.
I see again the dirty, musty walls
As now it passes through the darkened halls.
I hear once more the squeak of rusty chain
And realize that I'm awake again.
A key turns in a lock of odd-shaped form
Wheels clang and thunder as if from a storm

I dream and think all through the beauteous day
Till twilight makes a golden, sparkling door
And when I feel sleep come stealing o'er,
Then I close my eyes wove with lacework fine
To search for peace. A Prison is my mind.

THE UNANSWERABLE QUESTION
Stanley Schultz

How many years 'til war shall end;
How many millions must we spend,
How many boys will we have to send
'Til Peace shall reign again?

How many nations more will fall;
How many people for help will call;
How many decades until we all
See Peace on earth again?

How many children will suffer and die;
How many hopes must our youth deny;
How many nations will shout the cry,
"There's Peace on Earth Again."

THE SEA IS A HORSE   Gaye La Guire

The thunderings of surf are his hoofbeats;
　The crests of foam his mane;
The salt sea spray his flying tail,
　And The Sea Wind is his name.

The sea-birds are his playmates,
　The emerald waters his eyes;
The sandy beaches his range,
　And his blankets are the skies.

The dashings of waves are his spirit,
　The clear sea-airs his breath;
The grey clouds were his making,
　And the grey rocks are his death

HOUSE OF LOVE   Carolyn Peck

I'll not build a palace of stone,
Nor brick, nor wood for my very own.
Rather I'll build it of joy and love,
Of the beautiful moon and stars above.

I'll build it of dreams and sorrows too;
With music and laughter I'll furnish it through.
Peace and contentment, a happy heart,
These are the things with which I'll start.

All these things, with them, I will build
A happy home with joy be filled.
No, I'll not have a home of cold, dark stone,
But a warm house of love for my very own.

TOMORROW   Robert W. Upshaw

The moaning wind, the dying sun,
These things I see and hear.
With humble stance and penitence,
I await the passing of the year.

Then with the dawn and rebirth of day,
The heavy weight is lifted.
As through the running sands of time,
All troubles and sorrows are sifted.

O mortal, gaze not upon thy past,
Seek not to re-live thy sorrow.
Turn, turn to the bright new day,
And live always for the morrow.

DEEP DESTINY   Elaine M. Hovorka

What mysteries are held in depth!
What beauty in the deep of color, pattern, dimension -
What glory in the depth of love, faith, and good -
How shallow mediocrity -
Yet depth extends in all directions,
Encompassing evil as well as good.

Man must choose his path through the circular corridors.
By his ways shall a man be judged.

Remember ...
How infinitely deep that unfathomable well of eternity
From which we are destined
To forever drink.

CREED   Don Thetford

To speak, but speak not words of God.
To sing, but sing not words of love.
To see, but see not beauties of life.
To hear, but hear not.

To feel, but feel only death.
To walk, but walk the road of sin.
To breathe, but breathe the airs of "Hell."
To sleep, but sleep not.

Do not these, but love all.
Do not these, but forgive all men.
Do not these, but believe with all thy heart.
Do not these, but live.

AMERICA'S SECOND ANSWER
                Owen Van Brocklin

We dropped the torch, ye Flanders' dead,
And now there's roaring o'er your head
Of battles fought in vain -
Fought for peace to come again.
The poppies blowing row on row
Are trampled as we meet our foe.
The promise we have broken
Again for peace our guns have spoken,
            In Flander's fields.

Rest again, for it is over.
Yes, over for evermore, it's over
And freedom is for you and me.
We will keep it true to thee
A lesson we have learned again,
            In Flander's fields.

I WONDER   Kay Harrell

What are the cool breezes speaking about,
    As they whisper through the trees?
Do they tell of places they have seen
    Far across the seas?

What are the spring flowers trying to say,
    As their heads nod up and down?
Are they trying to tell of the things they saw
    Before they crept up through the ground?

THE BLIND POET   Douglas Smith

In the wind
The darkened trees
Become stained with beauty -
Beauty I cannot see -
And the fear that was once God
Burns and flames deep within my eyes.
The wind gathers the withered leaves within its hand
And flings them
Against the soft earth and twisted trees
Where life hangs proudly for a moment
By a breath of wind.
Thus another leaf has fallen -
    Another light has gone out.
But yet, in their sorrow
No outcry the trees will extend
Except for hope the night will end, and once more
They may see
The soft challenge of green leaves
Against the wind.
    Pity me!
For this is the story of life;
This is a song of man . . .

IS IT LOST?   Candida Pilla

What makes peasant rise above queen?
That priceless quality rarely seen,
For which we seek but seldom find
Buried deep in the heart of all mankind.

What prompts the smile of the Omnipotent?
One virtue, the most magnificent!
What an ideal universe, ours could be,
If we all possessed it, charity!

MUTE WORLD   Hope Townley

Skinned to inertia
Of pain dimmed living
By the Judas hours
Breath - only the heart's pain.
Solitude-stabbed by they who birth
Cruel mouthing of taunt.
The child retreats, quiet
To her realm of fantasy,
Girdled in false peace.
Do you wonder why?

FOR I AM YOUNG   Barbara Booth

Age sees youth as a joyous fling
About which love and laughter cling.
It sees youth as a joyous elf
Who sings sweet songs to please himself.
It sees his laughing sparkling eyes
Which take earth's wonders with surprise.
Age sees youth with wings unfurled
With untramelled feet gently whirled.
It thinks him free from cares and woes,
And no fears it thinks he knows.
Because his fears and longings find no tongue,
But I knew them for I am young.

YOUTH   Geraldine Schmitz

He stands
        alone,
    On the brink of time,
        restless,
            pensive,
                and waiting.
I stand
    by his side,
        praying,
            believing,
                yet uncertain.
The future
    a chasm,
    Potential dreams
        half molded
            in our today
        lost
            in the threat
                of tomorrow.

PROMISE   Sandra Perl

I see promise in the world
Of better things, new banners,
Even in the midst of war and hunger
Man is seeking the best of life.

So I look in the future, the years ahead
When man will no more fight with man,
And the bird of peace will make its stand
On every flag in every land.

LONELINESS   Laura Everett McDonald

The fire is low and the lights are dim,
    And the music is soft and sweet.
I watch the dancing shadows flicker,
    And I am lonely.

My thoughts wander to loves I have known,
    Known in vain, for there was no response.
Loves taking me to my own little world,
    Free from care and worry.

I know not how my life shall pass,
    What happiness or sadness I shall endure,
But life is so precious, so loved by me,
    Every moment shall be a treasure.

The room grows chill, another day has passed -
    One more day in the life I love.
Sometimes happy and sometimes sad, I meditate,
    And I am lonely.

NIGHT   Betty K. White

Looming up from nowhere,
Wearing black chiffon,
Flinging stars far in space,
The night is coming on.

Sketching eerie shadows,
Parading queenly grace,
The night, proud in glory,
Weaves clouds of filmy lace.

THE SPRING Charlie Guest

The spring is a bubbling talkative thing!
It lies in the meadow mist
Its voice is pure as the song it sings
Of spring time and summer's twist
It sings to the birds and the birds sing back
Of antelope graceful and swift
Who come to drink at the spring's sweet brink
Then raise their heads and drift
It talks to the meadows and they laugh
It sings to the cows and the woolly calves
Laughs at the colt and the colt kicks
Then scampers away through the briar sticks.

DAFFODILS IN THE SNOW Janet Sue Shreut

Oh daffodils with thy golden grace
Winter, that had just slipped around the corner
And caught a glimpse of thee,
Has stolen back to try to hide thy beauty
With an icy blanket of snowy jealousies.

But even though she tried to hide
The beauty she thus found,
You stand courageously tall and graceful,
Your tender green raiment
Swaying gently below the beauty
Of your golden crown.

FIFTEEN Virginia Brennen

I am fifteen,
An age of inbetween,
A garden of memories behind
A lifetime ahead.

It is a magic age - fifteen
A year of the first tastes of the future
So wonderful and yet holding a little sadness,
For the carefree time of childhood that will
Fade in to memory.

An age of moods - fifteen
A moment of unexplainable joy
Then a sudden reverse, a tear
And longing for the child of other years
Oh, for the person of the future.

DOWN THE SUSQUEHANNA   Richard Sell

A shallow river and a mountain high,
Was what we saw as we rowed nearby.
Many dear their color just like rust,
We saw every day in clouds of dust.
Through the deep gorges of high mountains,
Past big rocks which sprayed water like fountains,
Onward, onward we came to a plain
With acres and acres of waving grain,
Through great big cities wide and tall,
Where once the Indians heard nature's call,
Around the high and powerful dams,
And then on through the beds of clams -
Rowing through this place so big and great
I'm proud to call this place my state.

BY THE SEA   Jane M. Duke

When standing by the sea all, all alone
Your toes in the sand, the blowing wind in your face,
And the feeling of freedom is your very own
As that of the sea gull who has left his base.
Then you begin to listen to the waves
As they roar and roll, then hum and drum galore
Like giants while they are sleeping and snoring in caves;
This continues while the waves are pounding ashore.
The sea gulls gliding through the air with ease,
The beauty of glistening, glittering, shapely shells,
And the frothy foam dancing on the shore as leaves -
All this makes up the sea with its salty, sanguine smells.
What a feeling of exultation it would be
If only mankind were so brave, guiltless, and free!

SUGGESTION BY NIGHT'S COMPANIONS
                              Lauretta Norton
In the field is an inclination
    Beautified by tranquil night.
The lucid moon with sympathy
    Lends to earth celestial light.

In the background, trees are solemn
    Silhouetted against the sky.
Sprinkled with stars, they stand to pray
    In this velvet indigo dye.

The ecstatic beauty of the night
    Gives our restless world a peace.
Shall this be known to hostile ones
    When the Korean War shall cease?

BEAUTY Lillian Walsh

There are many types of flowers
    Of varied shape and hue
But beauty lies in the garden bowers
    Where mates the daffodil
        with the dew!

WIND James Koller

The wind
is a voice.
It can speak in anger,
for the wind destroys.
It can speak with gentleness,
for the wind knows gentleness.
And the voice can be still,
for the wind knows quiet.

TO THE WIND Joyce Ann Lucas

O wind, who hath
    From ages past
Kissed the cheek
    Of noble men,
And bit with equal vengeance
    the flesh of the
Thief in the night -

Are you always just
    And right,
Or do you sometimes
    Repent of having
Done, like lowly man,
    An act thoughtlessly
Mean, as driving your gale
    Over the spindly bridge
While man is striving to
    Endure the elements?

Yet, I know you counterbalance
    Your wrongs with rights,
As I begin to believe
    That man going to
Nature in time of doubt
    Strives to do. Yet, while he
Is weak, thou art mighty;
    Could it be that
Even the mighty are imperfect?

THE QUEST   Elsa Johner

I went to look for something they call Peace.
At first, I did not know just where to go
Along the city streets? I walked so slowly,
And wondered if my search would ever cease.
I found myself along a windy shore
But in the raging sea, could there Peace be?
And so, at night, there was no rest for me;
The longing in my heart grew more and more.
So, from Korea, now I heard a sound
Across the cold and blood-stained battlefields,
But where War is, there's never Peace, you see!
In a humble stable, there, my Peace was found
For, in the heart of Him whose hand has healed,
There is what true Peace shall always be!

SONNET   Carolyn Yates

Shall I compare thy tranquil beauty to
A lovely Christmas Eve, thine eyes sky-blue;
Thy soft blonde hair - an angel's halo's glow;
Thy rapt'rous voice that echoes 'cross the snow;
Thy pleasant laughter, warming souls of all,
As cheery as a Yuletide log. The hall
Is only bright as long as thou canst smile.
And as ye praise and sing, I all the while,
Thank God, that I, one humble lamb, in His
Great flock of life should have thou, peace, and bliss.
Thy head bows low with reverence to pray,
That peace on this great earth may reign someday.
I lift mine eyes unto You, Lord above -
So thankful of Thy gifts and wondrous love.

A WONDERING   **Naomi** Foster

Each evening when I close my eyes,
To drift on to another land,
In that soft mist, where day dreams rise,
I find wondering at hand.

When I grow bold in fantasy,
And open many doors
To see things daylight hides from me,
I go wondering for chores.

It's all so beautiful and new
So filled with promise fair,
And now it seems you too
Are wondering there.

THE WANDERER   Genevieve Metz

Oh, curse the blackness of this moonless night,
Each twisted tree, a monster in disguise.
Grim vapors rise and seem to beckon me,
Within foul bosoms there to grasp me tight.
My heart begins to pound within my breast.
My feverish mind fills with thoughts of doom.
The cruel wind, my lantern light has claimed.
I fear that now my homeward path is lost.
But, surely, God will lead me to my home,
Where all await and pray for my return,
For many has He helped to find the way,
To light and hope and - faith in Him restored.

AWAKENING   Elizabeth Smith

Look first to the brooks for Spring, my love,
    Where the shadblow first gleams white;
That we might see its petaled stars
    Emerging from the Night.

There the green-gray mists of Spring arise
    At the coming of the day
To meet the challenge of the sun -
    And swiftly melt away.

There first the blackbird calls, my love,
    A whispered song, a prayer -
A slender note, but hardly heard,
    Save by someone wand'ring there.

In answer a zephyr stirs the trees,
    They seem to stretch and yawn,
Imperceptably life is moving,
    Slowly, slowly to the Dawn.

TO THE MOON   Lorraine Yelle

Thou, graceful goddess of the night
Whose silver orb the clouds embrace,
O'er trees and meadows spread thy light,
And with thy silv'ry beams retrace
A sweeping path of argent bright.

Oh! lovely lady, if thou will,
Weave midst my fears your silver webs.
Dispel, as sand engulfs the rill
Deserted by the tide that ebbs,
Those lonely thoughts that linger still.

SEA MUSIC (A Fragment)   Marcus W. Sevier

That wide and wondrous water
Keeps calling unto me,
The clear voice of the daughter
Of all Infinity;
That deep and ceaseless music,
The music of the sea!

When deeply wrapped in sorrow
I walked along the quay,
And vainly sought to borrow
Some small security,
I found a deeper sorrow,
The sorrow of the sea!

I SHALL NOT   Beth Hatchett

What use is there in living?
I have no peace!
What use is there in dying?
I have no glory!
What use is there in loving?
I'll not be loved!
What use is there in caring?
For - who would care?

I could live.
        I could die.
                I could love.
                        I could care.

But - who would care?
I shall not

WHAT CAN WE DO?   Judy Dawson

Smoke
Moiling, belching, mushrooming
Up into the sky.
Bombs
Whistling, crashing, thundering
Death down upon us.
Do we want our world
To be nothing but smoke
And bombs
Ripping, slashing, tearing
The earth apart?
What can we do to stop it?
What can we do?

PAIN   Martha G. A. Johnson

Pain is a vicious monster,
It is hard to subdue;
It burns, it stings, it stabbs and aches
Until all the joy out of life it takes.

Pain knocks incessantly at the door of the heart,
Waiting - patiently waiting for an entrance;
Its continual gnawing ages and weakens the body -
Then, in stalks death with its hood of darkness,
And silently finishes the work that pain began.

YOUTH   Flora Farley

It is only once -
We can wade in bubbling brooks
Slipping from stone to stone
Laughing together
With the sun warm on our legs.

It is only once -
We can run through the tall grass
Stumbling through weeds
Gathering buttercups
While the robin sings over head.

It is only once -
When our hearts are young
Feeling the joy of Spring
Experiencing first love
With the past forgotten
And the future far ahead.

It is only once. Youth should be longer.

THE RAIN   Marie Louise Godart

I sat and watched the rain today
It fell so quietly
Disturbing not a single thing
Nor person, I could see.

It danced on top the highest roof
And kissed the earth below
Then slowly ceased and went away
To where, I'll never know!

NOVEMBER   Mary Ann Arceneaux

November's skies are pale and sullen
Dotted by puffs of cream-like clouds,
Slowly whipped into fluffiness by a playful wind
And stretching endlessly to bleak horizons
Like frosted icing on a layer cake.

November's nights are cold and dreary
Livened by honking blasts of great, wild geese
Flying on high; a radiant glow of silvery-tinted moonlight
Outlines the massive stiffness of their cold, white forms
As they noisily wing over marshy, dismal lakes.

November's days are short and cheerless
Deadened by a sudden loss of Autumn's gaiety,
And busily she dabs nature's greenery with forlorn hope
While restlessly shifting, heavily breathing
With the lifeblood of Winter's veins in her wake.

WHEN SHE SPEAKS   Carolyn Evans

When she speaks of justice,
    Her expression is wise,
When she speaks of cruelty,
    Her face looks as though she's hurt;
When she speaks of peace,
    Her expression is calm, tranquil;
When she speaks of a child,
    Her countenance is sweet;
When she speaks of two lovers,
    Her features are tender;
But how does she look
    When she speaks of me?

IN MY GARDEN   Rosemary McKenna

Gracefully,
Balmy breezes blow
Soft, swooping seas of fragrance
From the blooming blossoms,
Like feathers.
Bluebirds hopping between the rows
Blossom out in bold victorious melodies,
Calling:
"Mates and friends,
Come,
Let us share with you
What we have sought and found."

TRIALS OF NIGHT   Carol Colson

As the evening slowly steals upon us all,
A curtain falls and closes out the light.
The dark is thick and rises like a wall
And shuts us in as victims of the night.
The sun has gone and the wind begins to blow;
It shakes the trees and howls throughout the town.
A tree may fall and leave someone in woe;
Or the wind itself may blow some person down.
We stand in fear of the darkness over head
And pray for light to lead us on our way.
We pass the graves of those we know are dead
And o'er them hangs a weird and misty gray;
And while we're waiting for the dawn to break,
We think of tasks that we must undertake.

SUNRISE   Danny Sue Outlaw

The world is waiting now.
It seems to hold its breath.
Nothing stirs, no movement made -
It has the hush of death.

And then - a miracle happens!
A bird's refrain relates
The beauty of light that's coming -
The magic the sun creates.

The sun lights up a waking world,
The birds now madly sing.
The world is bright with light once more -
Old Sol again is king.

TO A ROSE   Robert Kramarz

Adorn my grave, O red, red rose,
   Thy beauty ne'er grows old;
Thy thorns, thy stem, thy opened bud
   Each petal and each fold.

Thy stem reminds me of my God
   With thorns that pierced His head;
Thy color - O so scarlet red
   His life-stream when He bled.

So don my grave, O reddest rose,
   Thy roots reach down for me;
And take me in thy bosom's care
   For All Eternity.

334

AN AUTUMN DAY   Carolyn Riddle

I walked with God today as I strolled in His glorious woods.
And He whispered to me through the wind in the trees
And I saw His face in a cloud.
Even the leaves heard the sound of His voice
And trembled in ecstacy.
They spread bright wings and drifted to ground
Where they sighed and sank to rest.
And the sun lay bright on the carpet of gold
And my soul climbed heavenward
On the song of a bird.

NIGHT   Glenn Tucker

It is quiet.
The blaring of horns and buzzing of traffic
Has ceased.
The eye has caught the last full rays of the sun
As it sinks behind its temporal prison.
Few lights blink,
Few doors creak,
Few minds think,
Few mouths speak.
The hungry dog lopes slowly down the dismal streets
In search of shelter from the cold.
The old town clock peals forth its low, haunting tones
Stirring an otherwise motionless world.
Few lights are burning,
Few wheels are turning,
Few minds are learning,
Few hearts are yearning.
Hushness prevails, Stillness is dominant.
It is quiet.

BY THE DYING EMBERS   Henry Simons

First the fire will kindle bright,
    Lighting all the tranquil night,
Then the sparkling rises high,
    Trailing smoke up to the sky,
Then the logs burst into blaze,
    Gleaming forth in pretty ways,
Soon the brightness will be past,
    All the sputtering does not last.
Then the embers slowly die,
    So we live, yes, you and I.

MUSIC   Glenn Tucker

Music is a dark, lean man walking in cold rain down cobblestone streets.
It is a beautiful, merry girl singing in tall, green clover.
It is a sense of danger, a sense of impending doom on a guilty man.
It is the stillness at the noontide, the lashing fury of a storm at night.
It is the thousand eyes of God sparkling in blue, cold night skies.
It is the roar of savage lions, the hushed voices of angels in Faith's presence.
Music is rough, hard, and cold.
Music is clean, pure, and holy.

TIME   Ruth Barry

A time for joy, a time for fun,
    Is enjoyed for a time each day,
A time to sit, a time to run
    This "time" is a sunset's ray.

For when a moment has passed away
    Never again to return
It's like the gone-by yesterday
    Though for it you may yearn.

The hands of time take a rapid pace,
    A pace to be tried by all,
But time seems always to win that race
    The slow by the roadside fall.

RED SUNSET   Joan Rae Frank

Red sunset over hazy mountains,
A painter's dream come true.
One touch of God's hand,
And the clouds are a deep blue.

Red sunset over hazy mountains,
Two lovers hand in hand.
Opaque rays of gold dust -
Spreading over the land.

Red sunset over hazy mountains,
Lakes reflecting rays of light.
A masterpiece to be remembered,
For it shows up God's might.

SOPHIA   Michael Holquist

There is the tolling of a bell, the hanging of some crepe,
And the hole in the earth . . . .
Or the lighting of a fire.

Out in the swirling vastness of space, now in that great astral
Herd, there rests another soul,
Free of the prison that housed its beauty and that
Hid it with twistings and ugliness.
Free, that soul is now, to sing with the stars,
And to roam the corridors of eternity.

My garment is threadbare
And shapeless,
And I am girt in the sack cloth - of a broken heart.

UNFINISHED SYMPHONY   Ann Edith Pickles

And now there is music where there was none before.
Haunting and beautiful, it fills the hush
Fallen ower men.
There is life in that music,
There is laughter and heartbreak.
And there is work -
Ceaseless, relentless, bone-tiring struggle,
Effort written in notes on a page,
Translated into glory and beauty of sound,
Rising Heavenward, whence it came.
To write this music a man struggled;
He labored, wearied himself,
But still he labored, ever cleaving
To the beauty forming in his mind.
Before it was finished, before he triumphed,
He died.
But now there is music where there was none before.

THE QUESTION   Marjory Davis

Life comes to the wing of a bird,
And flies too swiftly by;
But when death comes to the bird,
Does anyone cry?

Life is rich as the freshest snow,
As bright as the noon-day sun;
But when the darkness comes on,
Is day done?

Life is a precious gift,
So fine, so full, so sweet;
So why should I question life,
When death I am yet to meet?

MORNING AFTER CHRISTMAS   JoAnn Black

A massive pile of broken boxes,
An endless line of tissue spread
From room to room like crushed snow,
Fringed satin and glazed bits of ribbon,
Candy sticks of red and white,
Droopy mistletoe and empty shells
Of partly nibbled nuts:
    Christmas morning - forgotten!

THE SUN SINKS LOW   Joyce Corne

The sun sinks low o'er the rolling hills,
When the cares of the day are done;
So do our lives, as we grow old,
And our sorrows and joys are won.

The world rests with a throbbing pulse
As dust steals o'er the land;
And our hearts beat high with love and joy
As we watch, at our souls' command.

The world and life are much alike
At the close of a long, long day;
The world rests with grace and peace,
And life quitely fades away.

OLD MEN'S THOUGHTS   Peter Hannon

Things weaken
And grow small
Turning gray
And hour
No longer flowers into hour
But a hair's thickness of breath
Is counted
And placed in a little box
To be bitterly recalled
As meaning so little
Yet fading so swiftly

When you are old
You think of death
As not
An infinite domain
But an end
A small and ugly tract of darkness
Perhaps beyond the littered alley's end
Behind the shabby paintless fence
With the garbage and the smell.

THE LAUGHING BOY TO THE WAR IS GONE   Bob Reesh

He was always laughing,
The lad who has gone to war.
I feel I shall see him no more:
He has gone.
He hopes to right the wrong
That people have hoped for so long.

He always laughed.
Now his life is but an empty dream.
He is one of many on whom we lean,
He loved life -
He will laugh again some day
When all the world is free and gay.

TO LINCOLN   Diana Scott

(Inspired by the Lincoln Memorial)

Above long stairs, a temple, marble-white,
Enshrined there sits our Lincoln and still wears
That look of understanding love. With cares
His brow is worn. Amidst the shadowlight
His knowing eyes, dark-rimmed, fatigued, still bright
Through hope and joy, with wisdom smile He tears
Our minds from self and naught. What mortal dares
To mock, to cheat, to lie, before this sight?
Where is the lofty truth for which he fought?
Is it forgotten in the hearts of man?
The prejudice of time he tried to break.
The joy of liberty for all he sought -
No matter what their race or creed or clan.
Why did we all this man's ideals forsake?

LOVE IS LIKE A MELODY   Morton Sachs

Love is like a melody,
A tune piped in the spring;
Fluted trills like daffodils
Through the meadow ring.

Love is like a melody,
Soft, plucked upon the lyre
By Grecian sprites who in their flights
Carry love's song higher.

Love is like a melody,
Drum, and trumpet blast;
Loud and strong, and never wrong
Love's song will ever last.

YESTERDAY   Marcia Belsher

Yesterday wore a bright red dress
And laughed and ran to dance with spring,
Like me.
Violets shyly nodded beneath the fern
And whispered secrets to each other,
While singing rapids sang praises to the sun,
Like me,
Yesterday.

Today was wrapped in gray chiffon
And slipped by unwanted, unnoticed,
Like me.
Forgotten, it hid beneath the fern and held
                    the wilted violets
And wept, quietly remembering the river's song,
Softly weeping for the dancing day of spring,
Softly sighing for a memory of love,
Like me,
Today.

                    Jean Kennedy Norris

            little memories
          like dust clinging
                in the
                crevices
             of the mind,
       still there when all the winds
           of mitigating time
            have blown away
              the surface . . . .

            LIFE   Patricia Newton

            Love is different,
            Sometimes strange,
            In its ever changing ways -
            And customs,
            In its ever passing powers
            And overwhelming desires
            It buries us deep in the rotting sod.
            It's sometimes strong, good -
            And full of life,
            But yet as the years go by
            It brings fear
            And strife,
            To those who doubt -
            The everloving -
            Word of God.

SOLITUDE   Richard Perrin

I am shut by myself within a dream,
And as the familiar faces go by
I reach out to touch them,
And they fade.
I hear their voices,
Yet I know not what they say.
I call to them and speak their names.
My words stand still in air.

SKI SONG   Beth Blakemore

The flight of a bird
O'er whitest space,
The whirr of hickory
Under tightened trace,
The lightness of body
Exhilaration of soul
Unhindered, unaided,
Winging low.
No sight, nor sound,
But earth's white
Touching heaven's blue,
Your heart is singing
When the flight is through.

THE LAWS OF MAN   Jon Harmon

Man's laws show as
Proud and unashamed,
Where stands he best humble,
With head bowed.
They set him apart,
Display his total ignorance;
And show him as naked
In the brilliant light of the Eternal.
They point to vast imperfections
Masked with a haughty air
Of pseudo-intelligence.

For a single phase of legality
He finds himself lost
In uncounted volumes of laws;
Where, indeed, but one is needed.

I am a man.
I look at myself,
Laugh, then cry,
And once more
Don my cloak of false wisdom.

IN SOLITUDE   Howard Lane

Have you ever sat in silence; all alone, in solitude?
Did you ever ponder on abstract things,
On vast destruction and princesses and kings?
Have you ever thought of years to come and of the past,
Or how to find happiness, and make it last,
And what will happen when this fast, fast
Race with time is through?
If you have thought of wonderful, far removed problems,
And wished you knew,
Then you too have felt the certain peaceful blessing,
That only can be found in silence; all alone, in solitude.

FINDING GOD   Kenneth Eriksen

Life holds no fear to me
For Your presence is my courage and my faith.

I find You in the beauty of the mountain lake,
A celestial background in the alpen-glow of sunset.

We meet unexpectedly when I am alone,
Enthralled by the melodious beauty of Beethoven.

In spring, with its renewed beauty of reincarnation,
I find Your message of immortality to me.

My joys, my hopes, my desires, my trials:
In these - my life - You are my Comforter,
            my Guiding Star - my Father.

SONNET ON MUSIC   Billy Joe Wilder

It is often asked by many:
"How do you listen to music?"
And rushing to posts with frenzy,
The pedantics begin their rhetoric,

"You listen as if a story
Were being unfolded before you,
And if the story gets boring,
Watch the conductor's deft cues. "

"They are wrong and sadly lacking, "
Some say. "Listen for sept chords and duplets,
For only by studying and learning
Can anyone know a great Heifetz. "

Some answer, "Listen to that which is pretty, "
And there lies the truth to this query.

KIDS IS TROUBLE   Jerry Hornback -

When I grow up an' so old
That I'll know what I'm doin' without bein' told,
I'll never get married an' raise lots o' kids --
Pa told me what trouble them little kids is!
"They'll set in yer lap an' rinkle yer clothes
An' get in yer hair." I guess Pa knows!
Pa told me, too, though, that kids was a joy-
'Specially the ones what was born little boys.
But knowin' myself, I think that's a lie,
'Bout raisin' them young uns bein' easy as pie.
So I'm gonna remember now, all through my days,
That kids is trouble - an' trouble don't pay!

TO MY MOTHER   Penley Porter

My life is a creation of your mind
It's molded fair according to your will
Your every wish and mood I strive to fill
And thus become your masterpiece, in kind.

Your faithful, helping hands my life have twined
And guided me along the way until
At last when you are gone, and I'm here still
I'll keep your mem'ry in my heart confined.

Your soft, unerring smile I'll ne"er forget,
Remember, too, your yet unwrinkled brow.
I love those virtues to your family known;
A worthwhile life you've led, all goals you've met.
A woman, you, to whom the world will bow,
May I not blight the perfect seed you've sown.

RAIN   Priscilla LeBoeuf

As a perfect symphony
You hear its faultless beats.
Nary a discord is heard,
All play in flawless harmony.
Never a chord that is blurred.
Strings swing as the wind bleats
And percussions toll so rightly.
Otherwise it could not be,
God is conducting, you see.

God sends rain for our pleasure.
Why not take a joyful measure?
Cheerful, happy can you be
No need to fret, as you see.

A WILD BIRD   Sandra Aguado

Though once a wild free thing, now you are jailed
Your bright and shining plumage is quite paled.
Your restless spirit says you must be free,
But here your sentence reads, "Eternity."
No crime did you commit, unhappy bird,
Though sweet your song, it should have gone unheard.
For mortals hearing your clear call,
Knew not you must be free to sing at all.

PICTURES AT SEA   Marion J. Lashbaugh

The phosphorescent wavelets part
    And curl in tiers
    Like the spaced boughs
    Of the symmetrical fir.

White spray flutters like fine lace
    As the sharp bow-iron
    Slices the unfathomable sea,
    Trimming the ebony expanse.

Waiting for the sun and wind
    To clear and brighten the horizon,
    Shore and clouds blend into one
    Impenetrable gray adventure.

THE WORLD NEEDS YOU   Colleen Iverson

    Nothing is lost
    In the things you do
    To shorten pain and stress;
        The load you free
        Runs out to the sea
    Of truth and happiness.

    In daily life
    You have your part
    To lesson another's load;
        To give your share
        To help one move
    Along that rough and rugged road.

    No matter how small
    Your place may be
    And contributions few;
        The world needs
        That helpful deed
    Which only you can do.

WAR   Frances Park-Lewis Bliss

Now in this hour of hate, I lie
And conjecture what seems undeniable fate -
The wrong path chosen,
The horror met full pace on,
The shifting space of gravity flung worlds,
The uneven ground on which to step,
The shoulders heaved together for this "most worthy cause" -
And all to vanquish, plunder, hate,
Corrupt and burn and slaughter
Heart and Soul, once pure, of perfect universe.

Louisa E. Salvo

Glory be to God for dappled things,
        pretty things; like angel's wings.
Glory be to God for the loveliest of trees,
        the wind and the roaring breeze
And all praise to Him for He created the dew.
The twinkle in an old man's eye; -
        He put that there too.
And He expressed His love - when He created the earth
        He breathed down and gave nature its birth.
But most of all, He gave us the pattern of life
        He created man and presented him a wife.
Glory be to God for life's emotions
        happy commotions and thoughtful notions.
Glory be to God for He put within us
        wondrous sensations and creative imaginations.
He manifested His love - when He did create
When all these things He did originate.

JUST THINKIN'   Jane Maudsley

Last night I got to thinkin'
Of the good that's come to me;
Of the things that I've been given -
Unworthy, though, I be!

And then I got to wonderin'
Why this should come about;
And then it struck me forcefully -
God expects a turn-about!

He's given me my everything,
And topped it with Himself;
And so I think I'll start right now -
By giving Him 'myself"!

A TEAR   Margaret Weis

A tear,
  Filled with grief and sorrow,

A tear,
  Bitter today. Forgotten tomorrow.

FRIENDSHIP   Marta Bethlenfalvy

Friendship is a fragile chain
Which breaks so easily;
The links will hold for years untold
If fastened carefully.

BLACK   Mary Walker

A black-haired menace
Cool and calculating,
A shrewd mind,
Relentless, untiring
Beating tomtoms
In a dance of death
Sorrow and loneliness
Choked off breath.
Flashing eyes
And dancing feet
Lord! How I dance!
Hey-bob-a-ree-bop
I'm all reet!
Make
    Me
        Stop!
The tigress
Crouches bold with hunger
The tigress
Waiting to spring
And the congo drums
Humm and sing
Louder
LOUDER
And closer to her lair
She leaps!
Booma-booma, booma-booma
Booma-booma, booma-booma,
Booma-booma, booma, booma,
The jungle is filled with their sorrow
For the chieftan's son
Young and strong.   The tom toms
The congo drums   And their song of death
At his footprints beat -   Sorrow and loneliness.

WIND   Bob Carpenter

The boughs bend sharply until they crack,
    As the wind sweeps by on some unknown track,
Rushing onward ever onward till skies are greyed with dust,
    Carried upward whirling madly in the bellow's wild lust,
Slowing, halting, then forward again,
    Stopping but a moment to cool the brows of men,
Bending wheat gently, then off on its path,
    As if in the grasp of a madman's wrath.

The sun speeds onward in its arc across the skies,
    Yet the wind never falters, yet the wind never dies;
And when twilight's evening shadows slowly steal across the land,
    The winds, they turn to breezes, churning gently desert sand;
In all of God's great kingdom no man has ever dimmed
    The power of the bellows, the rushing of the wind.

ETERNITY   Sarah Wolf

Death comes,
A lonely traveler;
He picks his prey
And beckons.

Into eternity
He leads us;
Into a strange
Never-ending world.

INFANCY   Marjorie Williams

Man creates material things,
But one thing he cannot make
Is an infant, sweet
With angel light within her eyes
And a Heavenly mist about her
This wonder only God creates,
And we on earth can only pray
That we can teach this precious child
The ways of God, so she
May someday bear a blessed babe
For God and her to share.
For God with each mother shares
The happy hours, and days of grief
So that her beloved one will grow
And have children of her own.
Thus life continues for young and old
But the biggest moment of one's life
Is when he beholds a little child.

WRITINGS   Judith Davis

How tiny are the letters on a finely printed page,
How small the ageless writings of a poet, prince or sage.
Like the glory of the father finely printed deep inside,
Little words but full of glory,
"Love thy neighbor, lose thy pride."

WINTER DAY   Patricia Whitney

The night is still, dark, and cold.
Snow glitters like diamonds below our feet,
And stars above our heads twinkle mockingly.
Tall trees, so naked by day,
Hide themselves in the velvet blackness.
Little streams, beneath their heavy load of snow,
Freeze into clear ice.
Through the darkness shine beacons of light,
Calling home all those who are abroad on nights like these.

WHY?   Jerry Bangham

I put a small black spot on a piece
        of white paper.
"What do you see?" I asked the people;
They answered, "A black spot."

And yet the white surface was much larger
        than the black.
"Why do you only see the spot?" I asked,
And they could not answer.

PRICELESS GEMS   Dolores Ehr

The trees as stately and green as emeralds stand;
Snow - glistening and bright as diamonds - swirls;
Firesides, red as rubies, radiate coziness,
While secrets are held as precious as pearls.

GROWING UP   Tony Padzunas

As a youth grows older,
Life ceases to be an adventure and
Seemingly becomes an obsession

CITY NIGHT   Grace Alpher

The evening
has metastasized
a cancer of a
once-quiet
sky
a profound and pungent black
has grown
a city of long shadows
is not prepared
to drown
in a
blackened mounting flood
but burns
glowing rings
in street lamps
and explodes
neons
mad with colors   lured by
to seem yet alive.   blinding
                          fantasy
The people do not sleep   they escape
the city is teeming   for the moment
with people   to them
like vermin   day is
they crawl in hordes   a gray mask
with fat   of habit
wads of newspapers   and night
under their   is fighting
arms   violent
Some   full of color
take   contrast
fancy   and
to the neons   chaos.